BIG BOOK OF

MATH

Practice Problems

Fractions & Decimals

by

Stacy Otillio & Frank Otillio

EMPOWERING CHILDREN
FOR A SUCCESSFUL FUTURE

TABLE OF CONTENTS

TABLE OF CONTENTS

SECTION

1

SIMPLIFYING FRACTIONS

11 worksheets
21 problems per sheet

Simplifying Fractions

Simplify.

1) $\dfrac{8}{88}$ = $\dfrac{1}{11}$

2) $\dfrac{28}{32}$ = $\dfrac{7}{8}$

3) $\dfrac{21}{28}$ = $\dfrac{3}{4}$

4) $\dfrac{16}{20}$ = $\dfrac{4}{5}$

5) $\dfrac{14}{18}$ = $\dfrac{7}{9}$

6) $\dfrac{28}{44}$ = $\dfrac{7}{11}$

7) $\dfrac{30}{54}$ = $\dfrac{6}{9}$

8) $\dfrac{49}{70}$ = $\dfrac{7}{10}$

9) $\dfrac{16}{40}$ = $\dfrac{4}{10}$

10) $\dfrac{40}{55}$ = $\dfrac{8}{11}$

11) $\dfrac{6}{8}$ = $\dfrac{3}{4}$

12) $\dfrac{4}{8}$ = $\dfrac{2}{4}$

13) $\dfrac{20}{28}$ = $\dfrac{5}{7}$

14) $\dfrac{18}{48}$ = $\dfrac{3}{8}$

15) $\dfrac{18}{75}$ = $\dfrac{3}{25}$

16) $\dfrac{5}{10}$ = $\dfrac{1}{2}$

17) $\dfrac{3}{6}$ = $\dfrac{1}{2}$

18) $\dfrac{10}{12}$ = $\dfrac{5}{6}$

19) $\dfrac{8}{100}$ = $\dfrac{4}{50}$

20) $\dfrac{20}{25}$ = $\dfrac{4}{5}$

21) $\dfrac{5}{50}$ = $\dfrac{1}{10}$

Simplifying Fractions

Simplify.

1) $\dfrac{56}{63}$ = $\dfrac{8}{9}$

2) $\dfrac{10}{35}$ = $\dfrac{2}{7}$

3) $\dfrac{48}{54}$ = $\dfrac{8}{9}$

4) $\dfrac{25}{35}$ = $\dfrac{5}{7}$

5) $\dfrac{21}{70}$ = $\dfrac{3}{10}$

6) $\dfrac{12}{18}$ = $\dfrac{2}{3}$

7) $\dfrac{12}{27}$ = $\dfrac{4}{9}$

8) $\dfrac{6}{33}$ = $\dfrac{2}{11}$

9) $\dfrac{4}{20}$ = $\dfrac{1}{5}$

10) $\dfrac{15}{25}$ = $\dfrac{3}{5}$

11) $\dfrac{35}{56}$ = $\dfrac{5}{8}$

12) $\dfrac{32}{100}$ = $\dfrac{8}{25}$

13) $\dfrac{3}{21}$ = $\dfrac{1}{7}$

14) $\dfrac{16}{88}$ = $\dfrac{8}{11}$

15) $\dfrac{21}{49}$ = $\dfrac{3}{7}$

16) $\dfrac{8}{12}$ = $\dfrac{2}{3}$

17) $\dfrac{8}{32}$ = $\dfrac{1}{4}$

18) $\dfrac{18}{45}$ = $\dfrac{6}{15}$

19) $\dfrac{35}{55}$ = $\dfrac{7}{11}$

20) $\dfrac{5}{10}$ = $\dfrac{1}{2}$

21) $\dfrac{6}{75}$ = $\dfrac{2}{25}$

Simplifying Fractions

Simplify.

1) $\dfrac{4}{8}$ = _____ $\dfrac{1}{2}$

2) $\dfrac{18}{22}$ = _____ $\dfrac{9}{11}$

3) $\dfrac{10}{12}$ = _____ $\dfrac{5}{8}$

4) $\dfrac{4}{6}$ = _____ $\dfrac{2}{3}$

5) $\dfrac{35}{56}$ = _____ $\dfrac{5}{8}$

6) $\dfrac{6}{10}$ = _____ $\dfrac{3}{5}$

7) $\dfrac{2}{4}$ = _____ $\dfrac{1}{2}$

8) $\dfrac{18}{30}$ = _____ $\dfrac{3}{5}$

9) $\dfrac{9}{33}$ = _____ $\dfrac{3}{11}$

10) $\dfrac{20}{24}$ = _____ $\dfrac{5}{6}$

11) $\dfrac{18}{20}$ = _____ $\dfrac{9}{10}$

12) $\dfrac{18}{24}$ = _____ $\dfrac{3}{4}$

13) $\dfrac{24}{44}$ = _____ $\dfrac{3}{5}$

14) $\dfrac{64}{72}$ = _____ $\dfrac{8}{9}$

15) $\dfrac{56}{77}$ = _____ $\dfrac{8}{11}$

16) $\dfrac{36}{42}$ = _____ $\dfrac{6}{7}$

17) $\dfrac{24}{32}$ = _____ $\dfrac{3}{4}$

18) $\dfrac{35}{45}$ = _____ $\dfrac{7}{9}$

19) $\dfrac{8}{12}$ = _____ $\dfrac{2}{3}$

20) $\dfrac{12}{42}$ = _____ $\dfrac{2}{7}$

21) $\dfrac{24}{75}$ = _____ $\dfrac{8}{25}$

www.claymaze.com

Simplifying Fractions

Simplify.

1) $\dfrac{14}{22}$ = _$\dfrac{7}{11}$_

2) $\dfrac{14}{50}$ = _$\dfrac{7}{25}$_

3) $\dfrac{10}{15}$ = _$\dfrac{2}{3}$_

4) $\dfrac{9}{54}$ = _$\dfrac{1}{9}$_

5) $\dfrac{12}{20}$ = _$\dfrac{3}{5}$_

6) $\dfrac{27}{75}$ = _$\dfrac{9}{25}$_

7) $\dfrac{3}{75}$ = _$\dfrac{1}{25}$_

8) $\dfrac{2}{4}$ = _$\dfrac{1}{2}$_

9) $\dfrac{24}{50}$ = _$\dfrac{12}{25}$_

10) $\dfrac{5}{15}$ = _$\dfrac{1}{3}$_

11) $\dfrac{15}{55}$ = _$\dfrac{3}{11}$_

12) $\dfrac{45}{72}$ = _$\dfrac{5}{8}$_

13) $\dfrac{36}{45}$ = _$\dfrac{4}{5}$_

14) $\dfrac{16}{28}$ = _$\dfrac{4}{7}$_

15) $\dfrac{5}{55}$ = _$\dfrac{1}{11}$_

16) $\dfrac{7}{77}$ = _$\dfrac{1}{11}$_

17) $\dfrac{18}{30}$ = _$\dfrac{3}{5}$_

18) $\dfrac{28}{36}$ = _$\dfrac{7}{9}$_

19) $\dfrac{45}{81}$ = _$\dfrac{5}{9}$_

20) $\dfrac{7}{49}$ = _$\dfrac{1}{7}$_

21) $\dfrac{10}{25}$ = _$\dfrac{2}{5}$_

Name _____ Date _____

Simplifying Fractions

Simplify.

1) $\dfrac{28}{44}$ = $\dfrac{7}{11}$ 2) $\dfrac{24}{75}$ = $\dfrac{8}{25}$ 3) $\dfrac{15}{21}$ = $\dfrac{5}{7}$

4) $\dfrac{12}{100}$ = $\dfrac{3}{25}$ 5) $\dfrac{8}{40}$ = $\dfrac{1}{5}$ 6) $\dfrac{12}{50}$ = $\dfrac{6}{25}$

7) $\dfrac{6}{9}$ = $\dfrac{2}{3}$ 8) $\dfrac{6}{21}$ = $\dfrac{2}{7}$ 9) $\dfrac{16}{24}$ = $\dfrac{2}{3}$

10) $\dfrac{6}{12}$ = $\dfrac{1}{2}$ 11) $\dfrac{32}{40}$ = $\dfrac{2}{5}$ 12) $\dfrac{24}{40}$ = $\dfrac{3}{5}$

13) $\dfrac{3}{15}$ = $\dfrac{1}{5}$ 14) $\dfrac{40}{72}$ = $\dfrac{10}{18}$ 15) $\dfrac{12}{33}$ = $\dfrac{4}{11}$

16) $\dfrac{63}{90}$ = $\dfrac{7}{10}$ 17) $\dfrac{7}{35}$ = $\dfrac{1}{5}$ 18) $\dfrac{21}{24}$ = $\dfrac{7}{8}$

19) $\dfrac{42}{54}$ = $\dfrac{7}{9}$ 20) $\dfrac{27}{75}$ = $\dfrac{9}{25}$ 21) $\dfrac{12}{18}$ = $\dfrac{2}{3}$

6

www.claymaze.com

Simplifying Fractions

Simplify.

1) $\dfrac{36}{100}$ = $\dfrac{18}{50}$

2) $\dfrac{18}{22}$ = $\dfrac{9}{11}$

3) $\dfrac{6}{24}$ = $\dfrac{1}{4}$

4) $\dfrac{5}{40}$ = $\dfrac{1}{8}$

5) $\dfrac{32}{36}$ = $\dfrac{8}{9}$

6) $\dfrac{2}{4}$ = $\dfrac{1}{2}$

7) $\dfrac{16}{28}$ = $\dfrac{4}{7}$

8) $\dfrac{9}{90}$ = $\dfrac{1}{10}$

9) $\dfrac{6}{15}$ = $\dfrac{2}{5}$

10) $\dfrac{8}{18}$ = $\dfrac{4}{9}$

11) $\dfrac{3}{15}$ = $\dfrac{1}{5}$

12) $\dfrac{36}{42}$ = $\dfrac{6}{7}$

13) $\dfrac{5}{50}$ = $\dfrac{1}{10}$

14) $\dfrac{14}{22}$ = $\dfrac{7}{11}$

15) $\dfrac{4}{12}$ = $\dfrac{1}{3}$

16) $\dfrac{12}{50}$ = $\dfrac{6}{25}$

17) $\dfrac{4}{8}$ = $\dfrac{1}{2}$

18) $\dfrac{24}{36}$ = $\dfrac{1}{3}$

19) $\dfrac{18}{21}$ = $\dfrac{6}{7}$

20) $\dfrac{16}{50}$ = $\dfrac{8}{25}$

21) $\dfrac{15}{20}$ = $\dfrac{3}{4}$

Simplifying Fractions

Simplify.

1) $\dfrac{12}{30}$ = _____

2) $\dfrac{6}{12}$ = _____

3) $\dfrac{48}{66}$ = _____

4) $\dfrac{7}{28}$ = _____

5) $\dfrac{12}{18}$ = _____

6) $\dfrac{5}{20}$ = _____

7) $\dfrac{27}{33}$ = _____

8) $\dfrac{15}{25}$ = _____

9) $\dfrac{12}{54}$ = _____

10) $\dfrac{8}{20}$ = _____

11) $\dfrac{8}{14}$ = _____

12) $\dfrac{24}{75}$ = _____

13) $\dfrac{9}{81}$ = _____

14) $\dfrac{10}{22}$ = _____

15) $\dfrac{45}{63}$ = _____

16) $\dfrac{16}{24}$ = _____

17) $\dfrac{20}{25}$ = _____

18) $\dfrac{35}{40}$ = _____

19) $\dfrac{6}{48}$ = _____

20) $\dfrac{5}{10}$ = _____

21) $\dfrac{14}{63}$ = _____

Simplifying Fractions

Simplify.

1) $\dfrac{4}{6} =$ _____

2) $\dfrac{18}{30} =$ _____

3) $\dfrac{40}{55} =$ _____

4) $\dfrac{6}{22} =$ _____

5) $\dfrac{20}{24} =$ _____

6) $\dfrac{6}{24} =$ _____

7) $\dfrac{9}{45} =$ _____

8) $\dfrac{9}{33} =$ _____

9) $\dfrac{18}{81} =$ _____

10) $\dfrac{15}{27} =$ _____

11) $\dfrac{54}{60} =$ _____

12) $\dfrac{27}{45} =$ _____

13) $\dfrac{3}{33} =$ _____

14) $\dfrac{9}{18} =$ _____

15) $\dfrac{9}{54} =$ _____

16) $\dfrac{7}{14} =$ _____

17) $\dfrac{4}{50} =$ _____

18) $\dfrac{32}{72} =$ _____

19) $\dfrac{16}{100} =$ _____

20) $\dfrac{6}{36} =$ _____

21) $\dfrac{32}{40} =$ _____

Simplifying Fractions

Simplify.

1) $\dfrac{2}{6}$ = _____

2) $\dfrac{10}{12}$ = _____

3) $\dfrac{25}{40}$ = _____

4) $\dfrac{7}{35}$ = _____

5) $\dfrac{21}{77}$ = _____

6) $\dfrac{7}{21}$ = _____

7) $\dfrac{72}{80}$ = _____

8) $\dfrac{10}{35}$ = _____

9) $\dfrac{4}{18}$ = _____

10) $\dfrac{15}{25}$ = _____

11) $\dfrac{27}{36}$ = _____

12) $\dfrac{3}{9}$ = _____

13) $\dfrac{45}{55}$ = _____

14) $\dfrac{24}{30}$ = _____

15) $\dfrac{27}{90}$ = _____

16) $\dfrac{10}{15}$ = _____

17) $\dfrac{72}{81}$ = _____

18) $\dfrac{16}{50}$ = _____

19) $\dfrac{56}{80}$ = _____

20) $\dfrac{27}{75}$ = _____

21) $\dfrac{4}{6}$ = _____

Simplifying Fractions

Simplify.

1) $\dfrac{4}{10}$ = _____

2) $\dfrac{30}{54}$ = _____

3) $\dfrac{25}{50}$ = _____

4) $\dfrac{4}{8}$ = _____

5) $\dfrac{8}{40}$ = _____

6) $\dfrac{15}{20}$ = _____

7) $\dfrac{14}{21}$ = _____

8) $\dfrac{6}{8}$ = _____

9) $\dfrac{18}{42}$ = _____

10) $\dfrac{4}{14}$ = _____

11) $\dfrac{64}{88}$ = _____

12) $\dfrac{9}{81}$ = _____

13) $\dfrac{72}{88}$ = _____

14) $\dfrac{32}{40}$ = _____

15) $\dfrac{10}{16}$ = _____

16) $\dfrac{15}{18}$ = _____

17) $\dfrac{9}{63}$ = _____

18) $\dfrac{15}{27}$ = _____

19) $\dfrac{20}{44}$ = _____

20) $\dfrac{8}{32}$ = _____

21) $\dfrac{14}{35}$ = _____

Simplifying Fractions

Simplify.

1) $\dfrac{8}{18} =$ _____

2) $\dfrac{24}{80} =$ _____

3) $\dfrac{16}{56} =$ _____

4) $\dfrac{27}{75} =$ _____

5) $\dfrac{7}{14} =$ _____

6) $\dfrac{8}{22} =$ _____

7) $\dfrac{4}{36} =$ _____

8) $\dfrac{9}{54} =$ _____

9) $\dfrac{6}{12} =$ _____

10) $\dfrac{4}{12} =$ _____

11) $\dfrac{15}{33} =$ _____

12) $\dfrac{49}{63} =$ _____

13) $\dfrac{25}{75} =$ _____

14) $\dfrac{4}{32} =$ _____

15) $\dfrac{42}{56} =$ _____

16) $\dfrac{63}{70} =$ _____

17) $\dfrac{35}{40} =$ _____

18) $\dfrac{15}{27} =$ _____

19) $\dfrac{4}{10} =$ _____

20) $\dfrac{10}{18} =$ _____

21) $\dfrac{15}{20} =$ _____

SECTION

EQUIVALENT FRACTIONS

11 worksheets
21 problems per sheet

Equivalent Fractions

Complete the equivalent fractions.

1) $\dfrac{}{8} = \dfrac{32}{64}$

2) $\dfrac{5}{11} = \dfrac{}{99}$

3) $\dfrac{8}{} = \dfrac{56}{70}$

4) $\dfrac{9}{11} = \dfrac{36}{}$

5) $\dfrac{}{8} = \dfrac{54}{72}$

6) $\dfrac{5}{9} = \dfrac{35}{}$

7) $\dfrac{8}{} = \dfrac{16}{200}$

8) $\dfrac{8}{10} = \dfrac{}{50}$

9) $\dfrac{}{12} = \dfrac{18}{24}$

10) $\dfrac{4}{8} = \dfrac{}{32}$

11) $\dfrac{}{11} = \dfrac{72}{99}$

12) $\dfrac{8}{9} = \dfrac{16}{}$

13) $\dfrac{}{7} = \dfrac{25}{35}$

14) $\dfrac{6}{12} = \dfrac{}{36}$

15) $\dfrac{9}{} = \dfrac{54}{66}$

16) $\dfrac{8}{12} = \dfrac{24}{}$

17) $\dfrac{8}{} = \dfrac{56}{77}$

18) $\dfrac{4}{8} = \dfrac{}{16}$

19) $\dfrac{}{100} = \dfrac{20}{400}$

20) $\dfrac{7}{9} = \dfrac{14}{}$

21) $\dfrac{}{10} = \dfrac{36}{40}$

Name _____ Date _____

Equivalent Fractions

Complete the equivalent fractions.

1) $\dfrac{}{8} = \dfrac{21}{24}$

2) $\dfrac{5}{11} = \dfrac{}{55}$

3) $\dfrac{7}{} = \dfrac{21}{27}$

4) $\dfrac{9}{11} = \dfrac{72}{}$

5) $\dfrac{}{8} = \dfrac{36}{48}$

6) $\dfrac{9}{100} = \dfrac{18}{}$

7) $\dfrac{7}{} = \dfrac{28}{48}$

8) $\dfrac{9}{25} = \dfrac{}{50}$

9) $\dfrac{}{8} = \dfrac{35}{40}$

10) $\dfrac{5}{6} = \dfrac{}{12}$

11) $\dfrac{}{7} = \dfrac{24}{28}$

12) $\dfrac{4}{25} = \dfrac{8}{}$

13) $\dfrac{}{8} = \dfrac{40}{64}$

14) $\dfrac{7}{25} = \dfrac{}{75}$

15) $\dfrac{7}{} = \dfrac{14}{200}$

16) $\dfrac{9}{12} = \dfrac{27}{}$

17) $\dfrac{6}{} = \dfrac{12}{14}$

18) $\dfrac{4}{8} = \dfrac{}{72}$

19) $\dfrac{}{100} = \dfrac{12}{200}$

20) $\dfrac{8}{10} = \dfrac{40}{}$

21) $\dfrac{}{11} = \dfrac{36}{44}$

www.claymaze.com

Equivalent Fractions

Complete the equivalent fractions.

1) $\dfrac{}{100} = \dfrac{12}{300}$

2) $\dfrac{9}{10} = \dfrac{}{20}$

3) $\dfrac{8}{} = \dfrac{32}{100}$

4) $\dfrac{7}{9} = \dfrac{14}{}$

5) $\dfrac{}{25} = \dfrac{36}{100}$

6) $\dfrac{9}{100} = \dfrac{36}{}$

7) $\dfrac{9}{} = \dfrac{18}{50}$

8) $\dfrac{4}{12} = \dfrac{}{36}$

9) $\dfrac{}{11} = \dfrac{27}{33}$

10) $\dfrac{4}{6} = \dfrac{}{12}$

11) $\dfrac{}{8} = \dfrac{45}{72}$

12) $\dfrac{5}{100} = \dfrac{20}{}$

13) $\dfrac{}{9} = \dfrac{48}{72}$

14) $\dfrac{9}{100} = \dfrac{}{300}$

15) $\dfrac{7}{} = \dfrac{14}{24}$

16) $\dfrac{9}{10} = \dfrac{81}{}$

17) $\dfrac{5}{} = \dfrac{25}{30}$

18) $\dfrac{9}{10} = \dfrac{}{70}$

19) $\dfrac{}{7} = \dfrac{48}{56}$

20) $\dfrac{7}{10} = \dfrac{42}{}$

21) $\dfrac{}{12} = \dfrac{12}{24}$

Equivalent Fractions

Complete the equivalent fractions.

1) $\dfrac{}{12} = \dfrac{12}{36}$

2) $\dfrac{9}{11} = \dfrac{}{77}$

3) $\dfrac{6}{} = \dfrac{18}{21}$

4) $\dfrac{6}{9} = \dfrac{54}{}$

5) $\dfrac{}{25} = \dfrac{18}{50}$

6) $\dfrac{8}{100} = \dfrac{32}{}$

7) $\dfrac{7}{} = \dfrac{63}{90}$

8) $\dfrac{8}{11} = \dfrac{}{55}$

9) $\dfrac{}{10} = \dfrac{64}{80}$

10) $\dfrac{7}{11} = \dfrac{}{22}$

11) $\dfrac{}{6} = \dfrac{8}{12}$

12) $\dfrac{5}{8} = \dfrac{30}{}$

13) $\dfrac{}{10} = \dfrac{35}{70}$

14) $\dfrac{5}{12} = \dfrac{}{36}$

15) $\dfrac{7}{} = \dfrac{21}{300}$

16) $\dfrac{6}{11} = \dfrac{36}{}$

17) $\dfrac{9}{} = \dfrac{36}{100}$

18) $\dfrac{6}{9} = \dfrac{}{63}$

19) $\dfrac{}{9} = \dfrac{56}{72}$

20) $\dfrac{8}{10} = \dfrac{56}{}$

21) $\dfrac{}{25} = \dfrac{32}{100}$

Equivalent Fractions

Complete the equivalent fractions.

1) $\dfrac{}{12} = \dfrac{14}{24}$

2) $\dfrac{7}{25} = \dfrac{}{75}$

3) $\dfrac{4}{} = \dfrac{24}{42}$

4) $\dfrac{6}{8} = \dfrac{18}{}$

5) $\dfrac{}{11} = \dfrac{81}{99}$

6) $\dfrac{4}{8} = \dfrac{20}{}$

7) $\dfrac{5}{} = \dfrac{40}{48}$

8) $\dfrac{8}{12} = \dfrac{}{24}$

9) $\dfrac{}{11} = \dfrac{54}{99}$

10) $\dfrac{8}{9} = \dfrac{}{54}$

11) $\dfrac{}{10} = \dfrac{36}{60}$

12) $\dfrac{4}{8} = \dfrac{32}{}$

13) $\dfrac{}{100} = \dfrac{12}{200}$

14) $\dfrac{6}{11} = \dfrac{}{22}$

15) $\dfrac{8}{} = \dfrac{32}{100}$

16) $\dfrac{4}{7} = \dfrac{16}{}$

17) $\dfrac{4}{} = \dfrac{8}{24}$

18) $\dfrac{7}{100} = \dfrac{}{400}$

19) $\dfrac{}{9} = \dfrac{45}{81}$

20) $\dfrac{7}{25} = \dfrac{14}{}$

21) $\dfrac{}{7} = \dfrac{20}{35}$

Equivalent Fractions

Complete the equivalent fractions.

1) $\dfrac{}{8} = \dfrac{18}{24}$

2) $\dfrac{5}{7} = \dfrac{}{56}$

3) $\dfrac{9}{} = \dfrac{72}{80}$

4) $\dfrac{8}{100} = \dfrac{16}{}$

5) $\dfrac{}{25} = \dfrac{14}{50}$

6) $\dfrac{5}{11} = \dfrac{45}{}$

7) $\dfrac{8}{} = \dfrac{40}{50}$

8) $\dfrac{6}{100} = \dfrac{}{300}$

9) $\dfrac{}{9} = \dfrac{16}{36}$

10) $\dfrac{8}{11} = \dfrac{}{88}$

11) $\dfrac{}{25} = \dfrac{16}{50}$

12) $\dfrac{6}{11} = \dfrac{24}{}$

13) $\dfrac{}{8} = \dfrac{28}{32}$

14) $\dfrac{9}{10} = \dfrac{}{90}$

15) $\dfrac{7}{} = \dfrac{28}{48}$

16) $\dfrac{5}{100} = \dfrac{15}{}$

17) $\dfrac{5}{} = \dfrac{20}{100}$

18) $\dfrac{5}{11} = \dfrac{}{22}$

19) $\dfrac{}{12} = \dfrac{12}{36}$

20) $\dfrac{6}{9} = \dfrac{36}{}$

21) $\dfrac{}{25} = \dfrac{27}{75}$

Equivalent Fractions

Complete the equivalent fractions.

1) $\dfrac{}{8} = \dfrac{28}{32}$

2) $\dfrac{4}{25} = \dfrac{}{75}$

3) $\dfrac{4}{} = \dfrac{8}{10}$

4) $\dfrac{4}{9} = \dfrac{8}{}$

5) $\dfrac{}{10} = \dfrac{45}{90}$

6) $\dfrac{7}{9} = \dfrac{56}{}$

7) $\dfrac{6}{} = \dfrac{42}{77}$

8) $\dfrac{9}{12} = \dfrac{}{24}$

9) $\dfrac{}{25} = \dfrac{20}{100}$

10) $\dfrac{6}{10} = \dfrac{}{80}$

11) $\dfrac{}{11} = \dfrac{35}{77}$

12) $\dfrac{8}{9} = \dfrac{32}{}$

13) $\dfrac{}{9} = \dfrac{18}{27}$

14) $\dfrac{6}{7} = \dfrac{}{35}$

15) $\dfrac{9}{} = \dfrac{63}{77}$

16) $\dfrac{8}{25} = \dfrac{32}{}$

17) $\dfrac{5}{} = \dfrac{20}{400}$

18) $\dfrac{5}{9} = \dfrac{}{81}$

19) $\dfrac{}{100} = \dfrac{24}{300}$

20) $\dfrac{6}{25} = \dfrac{12}{}$

21) $\dfrac{}{12} = \dfrac{10}{24}$

Name _____ Date _____

Equivalent Fractions

Complete the equivalent fractions.

1) $\dfrac{}{11} = \dfrac{56}{88}$

2) $\dfrac{9}{25} = \dfrac{}{100}$

3) $\dfrac{8}{} = \dfrac{72}{90}$

4) $\dfrac{4}{100} = \dfrac{8}{}$

5) $\dfrac{}{12} = \dfrac{12}{24}$

6) $\dfrac{9}{100} = \dfrac{36}{}$

7) $\dfrac{4}{} = \dfrac{8}{50}$

8) $\dfrac{6}{11} = \dfrac{}{99}$

9) $\dfrac{}{9} = \dfrac{12}{18}$

10) $\dfrac{4}{9} = \dfrac{}{72}$

11) $\dfrac{}{100} = \dfrac{16}{200}$

12) $\dfrac{7}{25} = \dfrac{21}{}$

13) $\dfrac{}{25} = \dfrac{12}{50}$

14) $\dfrac{9}{10} = \dfrac{}{70}$

15) $\dfrac{8}{} = \dfrac{32}{36}$

16) $\dfrac{5}{9} = \dfrac{15}{}$

17) $\dfrac{4}{} = \dfrac{12}{36}$

18) $\dfrac{8}{100} = \dfrac{}{400}$

19) $\dfrac{}{11} = \dfrac{40}{55}$

20) $\dfrac{6}{100} = \dfrac{18}{}$

21) $\dfrac{}{25} = \dfrac{18}{75}$

Equivalent Fractions

Complete the equivalent fractions.

1) $\dfrac{}{10} = \dfrac{32}{40}$

2) $\dfrac{4}{5} = \dfrac{}{45}$

3) $\dfrac{4}{} = \dfrac{28}{63}$

4) $\dfrac{7}{25} = \dfrac{21}{}$

5) $\dfrac{}{9} = \dfrac{35}{45}$

6) $\dfrac{9}{10} = \dfrac{36}{}$

7) $\dfrac{7}{} = \dfrac{14}{20}$

8) $\dfrac{5}{100} = \dfrac{}{200}$

9) $\dfrac{}{5} = \dfrac{8}{10}$

10) $\dfrac{4}{100} = \dfrac{}{300}$

11) $\dfrac{}{7} = \dfrac{12}{21}$

12) $\dfrac{4}{8} = \dfrac{24}{}$

13) $\dfrac{}{12} = \dfrac{12}{24}$

14) $\dfrac{5}{6} = \dfrac{}{36}$

15) $\dfrac{8}{} = \dfrac{48}{60}$

16) $\dfrac{6}{25} = \dfrac{18}{}$

17) $\dfrac{9}{} = \dfrac{18}{20}$

18) $\dfrac{9}{12} = \dfrac{}{48}$

19) $\dfrac{}{6} = \dfrac{20}{24}$

20) $\dfrac{8}{12} = \dfrac{24}{}$

21) $\dfrac{}{100} = \dfrac{8}{200}$

Name _____   Date _____

Equivalent Fractions

Complete the equivalent fractions.

1) $\dfrac{}{12} = \dfrac{14}{24}$

2) $\dfrac{7}{10} = \dfrac{}{70}$

3) $\dfrac{4}{} = \dfrac{16}{20}$

4) $\dfrac{5}{11} = \dfrac{35}{}$

5) $\dfrac{}{100} = \dfrac{16}{400}$

6) $\dfrac{5}{25} = \dfrac{20}{}$

7) $\dfrac{5}{} = \dfrac{20}{400}$

8) $\dfrac{6}{12} = \dfrac{}{24}$

9) $\dfrac{}{100} = \dfrac{24}{300}$

10) $\dfrac{8}{11} = \dfrac{}{44}$

11) $\dfrac{}{25} = \dfrac{27}{75}$

12) $\dfrac{4}{12} = \dfrac{12}{}$

13) $\dfrac{}{9} = \dfrac{35}{63}$

14) $\dfrac{7}{100} = \dfrac{}{200}$

15) $\dfrac{9}{} = \dfrac{54}{66}$

16) $\dfrac{5}{8} = \dfrac{15}{}$

17) $\dfrac{5}{} = \dfrac{10}{12}$

18) $\dfrac{6}{100} = \dfrac{}{400}$

19) $\dfrac{}{7} = \dfrac{24}{28}$

20) $\dfrac{5}{8} = \dfrac{30}{}$

21) $\dfrac{}{10} = \dfrac{14}{20}$

Equivalent Fractions

Complete the equivalent fractions.

1) $\dfrac{}{12} = \dfrac{16}{48}$

2) $\dfrac{5}{11} = \dfrac{}{44}$

3) $\dfrac{5}{} = \dfrac{20}{100}$

4) $\dfrac{6}{25} = \dfrac{12}{}$

5) $\dfrac{}{9} = \dfrac{25}{45}$

6) $\dfrac{6}{12} = \dfrac{12}{}$

7) $\dfrac{9}{} = \dfrac{54}{60}$

8) $\dfrac{6}{12} = \dfrac{}{36}$

9) $\dfrac{}{100} = \dfrac{18}{200}$

10) $\dfrac{6}{9} = \dfrac{}{54}$

11) $\dfrac{}{11} = \dfrac{24}{33}$

12) $\dfrac{5}{9} = \dfrac{30}{}$

13) $\dfrac{}{12} = \dfrac{14}{24}$

14) $\dfrac{5}{7} = \dfrac{}{49}$

15) $\dfrac{9}{} = \dfrac{18}{24}$

16) $\dfrac{5}{7} = \dfrac{45}{}$

17) $\dfrac{7}{} = \dfrac{49}{77}$

18) $\dfrac{4}{6} = \dfrac{}{48}$

19) $\dfrac{}{10} = \dfrac{42}{70}$

20) $\dfrac{8}{9} = \dfrac{64}{}$

21) $\dfrac{}{10} = \dfrac{15}{30}$

SECTION

CONVERTING MIXED NUMBERS TO IMPROPER FRACTIONS

11 worksheets
21 problems per sheet

Converting Mixed Numbers to Improper Fractions

Convert the mixed numbers to improper fractions.

1) $8\dfrac{1}{12}=$ _____

2) $1\dfrac{8}{11}=$ _____

3) $4\dfrac{6}{8}=$ _____

4) $5\dfrac{3}{4}=$ _____

5) $4\dfrac{8}{9}=$ _____

6) $6\dfrac{9}{12}=$ _____

7) $3\dfrac{8}{9}=$ _____

8) $7\dfrac{3}{11}=$ _____

9) $4\dfrac{6}{10}=$ _____

10) $2\dfrac{6}{7}=$ _____

11) $3\dfrac{1}{9}=$ _____

12) $2\dfrac{3}{7}=$ _____

13) $5\dfrac{3}{9}=$ _____

14) $1\dfrac{3}{7}=$ _____

15) $3\dfrac{6}{11}=$ _____

16) $6\dfrac{7}{10}=$ _____

17) $8\dfrac{1}{8}=$ _____

18) $5\dfrac{7}{10}=$ _____

19) $3\dfrac{2}{5}=$ _____

20) $5\dfrac{4}{10}=$ _____

21) $7\dfrac{5}{7}=$ _____

Converting Mixed Numbers to Improper Fractions

Convert the mixed numbers to improper fractions.

1) $4\dfrac{6}{11} =$ _____

2) $5\dfrac{6}{7} =$ _____

3) $1\dfrac{6}{10} =$ _____

4) $6\dfrac{5}{9} =$ _____

5) $3\dfrac{4}{12} =$ _____

6) $7\dfrac{1}{7} =$ _____

7) $3\dfrac{1}{10} =$ _____

8) $5\dfrac{2}{3} =$ _____

9) $4\dfrac{7}{11} =$ _____

10) $2\dfrac{2}{12} =$ _____

11) $1\dfrac{3}{4} =$ _____

12) $2\dfrac{4}{9} =$ _____

13) $8\dfrac{2}{9} =$ _____

14) $5\dfrac{7}{10} =$ _____

15) $4\dfrac{1}{5} =$ _____

16) $5\dfrac{4}{8} =$ _____

17) $7\dfrac{7}{12} =$ _____

18) $5\dfrac{1}{10} =$ _____

19) $3\dfrac{8}{9} =$ _____

20) $4\dfrac{6}{7} =$ _____

21) $1\dfrac{1}{8} =$ _____

www.claymaze.com

Converting Mixed Numbers to Improper Fractions

Convert the mixed numbers to improper fractions.

1) $6\dfrac{1}{3}$ = _____

2) $1\dfrac{1}{12}$ = _____

3) $3\dfrac{3}{9}$ = _____

4) $7\dfrac{2}{8}$ = _____

5) $5\dfrac{4}{11}$ = _____

6) $1\dfrac{4}{8}$ = _____

7) $3\dfrac{2}{10}$ = _____

8) $2\dfrac{1}{3}$ = _____

9) $8\dfrac{8}{12}$ = _____

10) $7\dfrac{8}{11}$ = _____

11) $3\dfrac{1}{2}$ = _____

12) $7\dfrac{3}{9}$ = _____

13) $1\dfrac{2}{9}$ = _____

14) $6\dfrac{1}{4}$ = _____

15) $5\dfrac{1}{6}$ = _____

16) $5\dfrac{5}{7}$ = _____

17) $7\dfrac{7}{12}$ = _____

18) $3\dfrac{7}{11}$ = _____

19) $7\dfrac{5}{9}$ = _____

20) $5\dfrac{2}{7}$ = _____

21) $1\dfrac{3}{5}$ = _____

Converting Mixed Numbers to Improper Fractions

Convert the mixed numbers to improper fractions.

1) $2\frac{1}{11}$ = _____

2) $4\frac{6}{7}$ = _____

3) $2\frac{7}{11}$ = _____

4) $4\frac{3}{10}$ = _____

5) $6\frac{8}{11}$ = _____

6) $3\frac{7}{9}$ = _____

7) $3\frac{8}{11}$ = _____

8) $4\frac{3}{6}$ = _____

9) $1\frac{5}{12}$ = _____

10) $7\frac{6}{10}$ = _____

11) $6\frac{7}{8}$ = _____

12) $8\frac{7}{11}$ = _____

13) $6\frac{6}{8}$ = _____

14) $2\frac{5}{11}$ = _____

15) $5\frac{4}{9}$ = _____

16) $4\frac{5}{7}$ = _____

17) $6\frac{6}{10}$ = _____

18) $4\frac{5}{11}$ = _____

19) $8\frac{6}{9}$ = _____

20) $5\frac{6}{7}$ = _____

21) $3\frac{4}{6}$ = _____

Converting Mixed Numbers to Improper Fractions

Convert the mixed numbers to improper fractions.

1) $1\dfrac{8}{12} =$ _____

2) $2\dfrac{1}{11} =$ _____

3) $8\dfrac{6}{8} =$ _____

4) $8\dfrac{8}{11} =$ _____

5) $3\dfrac{7}{9} =$ _____

6) $5\dfrac{9}{12} =$ _____

7) $2\dfrac{2}{3} =$ _____

8) $4\dfrac{4}{5} =$ _____

9) $8\dfrac{1}{2} =$ _____

10) $3\dfrac{3}{8} =$ _____

11) $5\dfrac{1}{9} =$ _____

12) $6\dfrac{3}{10} =$ _____

13) $5\dfrac{3}{12} =$ _____

14) $7\dfrac{2}{11} =$ _____

15) $3\dfrac{2}{7} =$ _____

16) $2\dfrac{9}{10} =$ _____

17) $6\dfrac{9}{12} =$ _____

18) $8\dfrac{9}{10} =$ _____

19) $8\dfrac{7}{8} =$ _____

20) $1\dfrac{9}{10} =$ _____

21) $6\dfrac{5}{11} =$ _____

Converting Mixed Numbers to Improper Fractions

Convert the mixed numbers to improper fractions.

1) $2\frac{7}{8} = $ _____

2) $7\frac{6}{9} = $ _____

3) $2\frac{7}{12} = $ _____

4) $4\frac{2}{7} = $ _____

5) $1\frac{9}{10} = $ _____

6) $6\frac{7}{9} = $ _____

7) $3\frac{6}{8} = $ _____

8) $7\frac{1}{3} = $ _____

9) $2\frac{2}{10} = $ _____

10) $4\frac{3}{10} = $ _____

11) $2\frac{9}{11} = $ _____

12) $5\frac{8}{9} = $ _____

13) $2\frac{8}{11} = $ _____

14) $1\frac{3}{8} = $ _____

15) $7\frac{4}{6} = $ _____

16) $1\frac{1}{4} = $ _____

17) $8\frac{5}{6} = $ _____

18) $4\frac{2}{4} = $ _____

19) $4\frac{9}{12} = $ _____

20) $1\frac{7}{8} = $ _____

21) $3\frac{1}{11} = $ _____

Converting Mixed Numbers to Improper Fractions

Convert the mixed numbers to improper fractions.

1) $4\frac{3}{9} =$ _____

2) $5\frac{2}{5} =$ _____

3) $2\frac{4}{6} =$ _____

4) $8\frac{1}{8} =$ _____

5) $3\frac{3}{9} =$ _____

6) $7\frac{7}{12} =$ _____

7) $2\frac{2}{9} =$ _____

8) $1\frac{6}{7} =$ _____

9) $6\frac{2}{3} =$ _____

10) $4\frac{6}{11} =$ _____

11) $5\frac{7}{8} =$ _____

12) $3\frac{6}{12} =$ _____

13) $1\frac{5}{7} =$ _____

14) $2\frac{7}{11} =$ _____

15) $6\frac{3}{8} =$ _____

16) $5\frac{2}{4} =$ _____

17) $1\frac{6}{12} =$ _____

18) $4\frac{2}{6} =$ _____

19) $2\frac{5}{11} =$ _____

20) $3\frac{4}{9} =$ _____

21) $6\frac{8}{11} =$ _____

Converting Mixed Numbers to Improper Fractions

Convert the mixed numbers to improper fractions.

1) $5\dfrac{3}{5}$ = _____

2) $3\dfrac{8}{11}$ = _____

3) $6\dfrac{9}{12}$ = _____

4) $3\dfrac{6}{11}$ = _____

5) $2\dfrac{6}{9}$ = _____

6) $8\dfrac{2}{10}$ = _____

7) $6\dfrac{4}{9}$ = _____

8) $1\dfrac{5}{10}$ = _____

9) $5\dfrac{9}{11}$ = _____

10) $5\dfrac{3}{4}$ = _____

11) $3\dfrac{8}{9}$ = _____

12) $2\dfrac{7}{12}$ = _____

13) $4\dfrac{9}{11}$ = _____

14) $2\dfrac{2}{5}$ = _____

15) $3\dfrac{9}{10}$ = _____

16) $3\dfrac{2}{4}$ = _____

17) $2\dfrac{6}{11}$ = _____

18) $1\dfrac{5}{8}$ = _____

19) $2\dfrac{9}{12}$ = _____

20) $8\dfrac{1}{2}$ = _____

21) $6\dfrac{8}{12}$ = _____

Converting Mixed Numbers to Improper Fractions

Convert the mixed numbers to improper fractions.

1) $2\frac{4}{6} = $ _____

2) $7\frac{8}{12} = $ _____

3) $4\frac{4}{10} = $ _____

4) $4\frac{1}{9} = $ _____

5) $1\frac{6}{10} = $ _____

6) $7\frac{1}{5} = $ _____

7) $2\frac{1}{7} = $ _____

8) $6\frac{3}{8} = $ _____

9) $1\frac{4}{7} = $ _____

10) $5\frac{1}{11} = $ _____

11) $4\frac{9}{12} = $ _____

12) $6\frac{8}{10} = $ _____

13) $3\frac{2}{8} = $ _____

14) $6\frac{1}{11} = $ _____

15) $7\frac{1}{6} = $ _____

16) $4\frac{8}{11} = $ _____

17) $3\frac{5}{7} = $ _____

18) $8\frac{8}{10} = $ _____

19) $8\frac{5}{10} = $ _____

20) $5\frac{3}{9} = $ _____

21) $7\frac{1}{4} = $ _____

Converting Mixed Numbers to Improper Fractions

Convert the mixed numbers to improper fractions.

1) $5\dfrac{6}{12} = $ _____

2) $1\dfrac{8}{9} = $ _____

3) $3\dfrac{7}{10} = $ _____

4) $3\dfrac{7}{9} = $ _____

5) $4\dfrac{5}{10} = $ _____

6) $7\dfrac{4}{12} = $ _____

7) $6\dfrac{6}{7} = $ _____

8) $1\dfrac{6}{8} = $ _____

9) $4\dfrac{1}{4} = $ _____

10) $3\dfrac{4}{11} = $ _____

11) $4\dfrac{4}{10} = $ _____

12) $3\dfrac{1}{12} = $ _____

13) $7\dfrac{4}{7} = $ _____

14) $5\dfrac{3}{9} = $ _____

15) $4\dfrac{9}{10} = $ _____

16) $3\dfrac{8}{11} = $ _____

17) $4\dfrac{5}{12} = $ _____

18) $7\dfrac{1}{6} = $ _____

19) $7\dfrac{1}{7} = $ _____

20) $8\dfrac{6}{9} = $ _____

21) $6\dfrac{7}{12} = $ _____

Converting Mixed Numbers to Improper Fractions

Convert the mixed numbers to improper fractions.

1) $7\dfrac{3}{5}$ = _____

2) $5\dfrac{3}{12}$ = _____

3) $1\dfrac{8}{11}$ = _____

4) $4\dfrac{1}{12}$ = _____

5) $2\dfrac{4}{6}$ = _____

6) $8\dfrac{6}{10}$ = _____

7) $3\dfrac{5}{9}$ = _____

8) $5\dfrac{1}{12}$ = _____

9) $3\dfrac{2}{3}$ = _____

10) $8\dfrac{5}{11}$ = _____

11) $2\dfrac{4}{8}$ = _____

12) $8\dfrac{4}{5}$ = _____

13) $3\dfrac{7}{9}$ = _____

14) $8\dfrac{2}{12}$ = _____

15) $5\dfrac{3}{4}$ = _____

16) $5\dfrac{8}{12}$ = _____

17) $4\dfrac{5}{6}$ = _____

18) $1\dfrac{6}{12}$ = _____

19) $1\dfrac{3}{6}$ = _____

20) $6\dfrac{2}{4}$ = _____

21) $7\dfrac{7}{8}$ = _____

SECTION

CONVERTING IMPROPER FRACTIONS TO MIXED NUMBERS

11 worksheets
21 problems per sheet

Converting Improper Fractions to Mixed Numbers

Convert the improper fractions to mixed numbers.

1) $\dfrac{23}{3} =$ _____

2) $\dfrac{50}{11} =$ _____

3) $\dfrac{28}{5} =$ _____

4) $\dfrac{49}{8} =$ _____

5) $\dfrac{15}{2} =$ _____

6) $\dfrac{41}{12} =$ _____

7) $\dfrac{17}{9} =$ _____

8) $\dfrac{48}{11} =$ _____

9) $\dfrac{25}{3} =$ _____

10) $\dfrac{13}{4} =$ _____

11) $\dfrac{52}{9} =$ _____

12) $\dfrac{25}{4} =$ _____

13) $\dfrac{9}{2} =$ _____

14) $\dfrac{19}{12} =$ _____

15) $\dfrac{30}{11} =$ _____

16) $\dfrac{17}{5} =$ _____

17) $\dfrac{13}{2} =$ _____

18) $\dfrac{53}{6} =$ _____

19) $\dfrac{23}{10} =$ _____

20) $\dfrac{55}{12} =$ _____

21) $\dfrac{71}{11} =$ _____

Converting Improper Fractions to Mixed Numbers

Convert the improper fractions to mixed numbers.

1) $\dfrac{42}{11}$ = _____

2) $\dfrac{25}{3}$ = _____

3) $\dfrac{37}{9}$ = _____

4) $\dfrac{76}{9}$ = _____

5) $\dfrac{83}{11}$ = _____

6) $\dfrac{26}{3}$ = _____

7) $\dfrac{22}{5}$ = _____

8) $\dfrac{13}{10}$ = _____

9) $\dfrac{84}{11}$ = _____

10) $\dfrac{63}{11}$ = _____

11) $\dfrac{14}{5}$ = _____

12) $\dfrac{58}{7}$ = _____

13) $\dfrac{22}{9}$ = _____

14) $\dfrac{17}{12}$ = _____

15) $\dfrac{8}{3}$ = _____

16) $\dfrac{9}{2}$ = _____

17) $\dfrac{67}{9}$ = _____

18) $\dfrac{21}{4}$ = _____

19) $\dfrac{69}{10}$ = _____

20) $\dfrac{65}{12}$ = _____

21) $\dfrac{13}{3}$ = _____

www.claymaze.com

Converting Improper Fractions to Mixed Numbers

Convert the improper fractions to mixed numbers.

1) $\dfrac{7}{2}$ = _____

2) $\dfrac{23}{3}$ = _____

3) $\dfrac{9}{5}$ = _____

4) $\dfrac{4}{3}$ = _____

5) $\dfrac{13}{2}$ = _____

6) $\dfrac{25}{6}$ = _____

7) $\dfrac{67}{12}$ = _____

8) $\dfrac{60}{7}$ = _____

9) $\dfrac{89}{12}$ = _____

10) $\dfrac{11}{7}$ = _____

11) $\dfrac{19}{5}$ = _____

12) $\dfrac{20}{3}$ = _____

13) $\dfrac{17}{2}$ = _____

14) $\dfrac{11}{4}$ = _____

15) $\dfrac{80}{9}$ = _____

16) $\dfrac{17}{3}$ = _____

17) $\dfrac{3}{2}$ = _____

18) $\dfrac{33}{5}$ = _____

19) $\dfrac{9}{8}$ = _____

20) $\dfrac{22}{9}$ = _____

21) $\dfrac{15}{4}$ = _____

Converting Improper Fractions to Mixed Numbers

Convert the improper fractions to mixed numbers.

1) $\dfrac{19}{10} =$ _____

2) $\dfrac{60}{11} =$ _____

3) $\dfrac{5}{2} =$ _____

4) $\dfrac{38}{9} =$ _____

5) $\dfrac{4}{3} =$ _____

6) $\dfrac{81}{11} =$ _____

7) $\dfrac{37}{6} =$ _____

8) $\dfrac{31}{4} =$ _____

9) $\dfrac{20}{3} =$ _____

10) $\dfrac{61}{11} =$ _____

11) $\dfrac{59}{7} =$ _____

12) $\dfrac{43}{6} =$ _____

13) $\dfrac{11}{6} =$ _____

14) $\dfrac{13}{2} =$ _____

15) $\dfrac{7}{3} =$ _____

16) $\dfrac{53}{7} =$ _____

17) $\dfrac{17}{11} =$ _____

18) $\dfrac{31}{6} =$ _____

19) $\dfrac{23}{9} =$ _____

20) $\dfrac{45}{8} =$ _____

21) $\dfrac{47}{11} =$ _____

Converting Improper Fractions to Mixed Numbers

Convert the improper fractions to mixed numbers.

1) $\dfrac{37}{5}$ = _____

2) $\dfrac{79}{9}$ = _____

3) $\dfrac{9}{4}$ = _____

4) $\dfrac{48}{11}$ = _____

5) $\dfrac{38}{5}$ = _____

6) $\dfrac{59}{11}$ = _____

7) $\dfrac{47}{8}$ = _____

8) $\dfrac{30}{7}$ = _____

9) $\dfrac{37}{10}$ = _____

10) $\dfrac{97}{11}$ = _____

11) $\dfrac{63}{10}$ = _____

12) $\dfrac{21}{8}$ = _____

13) $\dfrac{13}{8}$ = _____

14) $\dfrac{25}{3}$ = _____

15) $\dfrac{16}{9}$ = _____

16) $\dfrac{27}{7}$ = _____

17) $\dfrac{6}{5}$ = _____

18) $\dfrac{36}{11}$ = _____

19) $\dfrac{14}{3}$ = _____

20) $\dfrac{58}{7}$ = _____

21) $\dfrac{22}{3}$ = _____

Converting Improper Fractions to Mixed Numbers

Convert the improper fractions to mixed numbers.

1) $\dfrac{25}{9}$ = _____

2) $\dfrac{3}{2}$ = _____

3) $\dfrac{26}{3}$ = _____

4) $\dfrac{15}{4}$ = _____

5) $\dfrac{27}{11}$ = _____

6) $\dfrac{37}{9}$ = _____

7) $\dfrac{89}{12}$ = _____

8) $\dfrac{27}{5}$ = _____

9) $\dfrac{19}{6}$ = _____

10) $\dfrac{55}{8}$ = _____

11) $\dfrac{14}{3}$ = _____

12) $\dfrac{61}{8}$ = _____

13) $\dfrac{19}{5}$ = _____

14) $\dfrac{18}{11}$ = _____

15) $\dfrac{23}{4}$ = _____

16) $\dfrac{8}{7}$ = _____

17) $\dfrac{23}{5}$ = _____

18) $\dfrac{14}{9}$ = _____

19) $\dfrac{75}{11}$ = _____

20) $\dfrac{17}{8}$ = _____

21) $\dfrac{53}{11}$ = _____

Converting Improper Fractions to Mixed Numbers

Convert the improper fractions to mixed numbers.

1) $\dfrac{11}{3}$ = _____

2) $\dfrac{80}{11}$ = _____

3) $\dfrac{9}{2}$ = _____

4) $\dfrac{13}{2}$ = _____

5) $\dfrac{37}{10}$ = _____

6) $\dfrac{20}{11}$ = _____

7) $\dfrac{38}{9}$ = _____

8) $\dfrac{85}{11}$ = _____

9) $\dfrac{15}{4}$ = _____

10) $\dfrac{30}{11}$ = _____

11) $\dfrac{67}{10}$ = _____

12) $\dfrac{22}{5}$ = _____

13) $\dfrac{26}{3}$ = _____

14) $\dfrac{11}{5}$ = _____

15) $\dfrac{47}{9}$ = _____

16) $\dfrac{63}{8}$ = _____

17) $\dfrac{69}{11}$ = _____

18) $\dfrac{69}{8}$ = _____

19) $\dfrac{74}{9}$ = _____

20) $\dfrac{27}{7}$ = _____

21) $\dfrac{8}{5}$ = _____

Name _____ Date _____

Converting Improper Fractions to Mixed Numbers

Convert the improper fractions to mixed numbers.

1) $\frac{5}{2}$ = _____

2) $\frac{34}{5}$ = _____

3) $\frac{30}{11}$ = _____

4) $\frac{39}{11}$ = _____

5) $\frac{19}{4}$ = _____

6) $\frac{71}{8}$ = _____

7) $\frac{7}{4}$ = _____

8) $\frac{19}{5}$ = _____

9) $\frac{61}{9}$ = _____

10) $\frac{41}{12}$ = _____

11) $\frac{53}{8}$ = _____

12) $\frac{31}{12}$ = _____

13) $\frac{29}{11}$ = _____

14) $\frac{11}{2}$ = _____

15) $\frac{27}{4}$ = _____

16) $\frac{41}{9}$ = _____

17) $\frac{90}{11}$ = _____

18) $\frac{9}{2}$ = _____

19) $\frac{87}{10}$ = _____

20) $\frac{39}{5}$ = _____

21) $\frac{11}{10}$ = _____

Converting Improper Fractions to Mixed Numbers

Convert the improper fractions to mixed numbers.

1) $\dfrac{68}{11}$ = _____

2) $\dfrac{43}{12}$ = _____

3) $\dfrac{9}{5}$ = _____

4) $\dfrac{5}{3}$ = _____

5) $\dfrac{19}{4}$ = _____

6) $\dfrac{7}{2}$ = _____

7) $\dfrac{23}{5}$ = _____

8) $\dfrac{61}{10}$ = _____

9) $\dfrac{31}{12}$ = _____

10) $\dfrac{14}{11}$ = _____

11) $\dfrac{5}{2}$ = _____

12) $\dfrac{14}{3}$ = _____

13) $\dfrac{27}{4}$ = _____

14) $\dfrac{71}{9}$ = _____

15) $\dfrac{57}{7}$ = _____

16) $\dfrac{21}{10}$ = _____

17) $\dfrac{16}{3}$ = _____

18) $\dfrac{63}{10}$ = _____

19) $\dfrac{25}{3}$ = _____

20) $\dfrac{25}{4}$ = _____

21) $\dfrac{21}{5}$ = _____

Converting Improper Fractions to Mixed Numbers

Convert the improper fractions to mixed numbers.

1) $\dfrac{74}{11}$ = _____

2) $\dfrac{10}{3}$ = _____

3) $\dfrac{71}{9}$ = _____

4) $\dfrac{55}{12}$ = _____

5) $\dfrac{89}{10}$ = _____

6) $\dfrac{12}{5}$ = _____

7) $\dfrac{33}{4}$ = _____

8) $\dfrac{83}{11}$ = _____

9) $\dfrac{59}{10}$ = _____

10) $\dfrac{65}{12}$ = _____

11) $\dfrac{31}{10}$ = _____

12) $\dfrac{17}{2}$ = _____

13) $\dfrac{25}{3}$ = _____

14) $\dfrac{53}{7}$ = _____

15) $\dfrac{8}{5}$ = _____

16) $\dfrac{11}{4}$ = _____

17) $\dfrac{25}{6}$ = _____

18) $\dfrac{89}{11}$ = _____

19) $\dfrac{79}{10}$ = _____

20) $\dfrac{42}{11}$ = _____

21) $\dfrac{22}{3}$ = _____

Converting Improper Fractions to Mixed Numbers

Convert the improper fractions to mixed numbers.

1) $\dfrac{11}{3}$ = _____

2) $\dfrac{53}{11}$ = _____

3) $\dfrac{31}{12}$ = _____

4) $\dfrac{53}{8}$ = _____

5) $\dfrac{18}{5}$ = _____

6) $\dfrac{87}{10}$ = _____

7) $\dfrac{91}{11}$ = _____

8) $\dfrac{47}{10}$ = _____

9) $\dfrac{23}{4}$ = _____

10) $\dfrac{24}{5}$ = _____

11) $\dfrac{95}{11}$ = _____

12) $\dfrac{11}{8}$ = _____

13) $\dfrac{93}{11}$ = _____

14) $\dfrac{91}{12}$ = _____

15) $\dfrac{41}{5}$ = _____

16) $\dfrac{13}{8}$ = _____

17) $\dfrac{35}{4}$ = _____

18) $\dfrac{17}{6}$ = _____

19) $\dfrac{20}{7}$ = _____

20) $\dfrac{31}{10}$ = _____

21) $\dfrac{20}{3}$ = _____

SECTION

COMPARING FRACTIONS

11 worksheets
21 problems per sheet

Name _____   Date _____

Comparing Fractions

Compare the fractions and write the correct symbol (<, = or >) in each box.

1) $\frac{9}{12}$ ☐ $\frac{1}{8}$

2) $\frac{3}{7}$ ☐ $\frac{5}{6}$

3) $\frac{2}{10}$ ☐ $\frac{9}{11}$

4) $\frac{4}{11}$ ☐ $\frac{7}{10}$

5) $\frac{1}{3}$ ☐ $\frac{2}{8}$

6) $\frac{4}{8}$ ☐ $\frac{28}{56}$

7) $\frac{1}{12}$ ☐ $\frac{5}{6}$

8) $\frac{7}{10}$ ☐ $\frac{8}{11}$

9) $\frac{7}{9}$ ☐ $\frac{4}{7}$

10) $\frac{4}{6}$ ☐ $\frac{9}{12}$

11) $\frac{4}{5}$ ☐ $\frac{3}{8}$

12) $\frac{8}{10}$ ☐ $\frac{2}{9}$

13) $\frac{3}{9}$ ☐ $\frac{7}{8}$

14) $\frac{6}{7}$ ☐ $\frac{3}{5}$

15) $\frac{5}{8}$ ☐ $\frac{3}{6}$

16) $\frac{45}{50}$ ☐ $\frac{9}{10}$

17) $\frac{3}{10}$ ☐ $\frac{9}{30}$

18) $\frac{5}{7}$ ☐ $\frac{4}{5}$

19) $\frac{5}{10}$ ☐ $\frac{1}{8}$

20) $\frac{4}{6}$ ☐ $\frac{7}{10}$

21) $\frac{9}{11}$ ☐ $\frac{2}{12}$

www.claymaze.com

Comparing Fractions

Compare the fractions and write the correct symbol (<, = or >) in each box.

1) $\dfrac{3}{7}$ ☐ $\dfrac{4}{10}$ 2) $\dfrac{7}{9}$ ☐ $\dfrac{49}{63}$ 3) $\dfrac{1}{4}$ ☐ $\dfrac{8}{10}$

4) $\dfrac{2}{8}$ ☐ $\dfrac{7}{11}$ 5) $\dfrac{9}{11}$ ☐ $\dfrac{4}{5}$ 6) $\dfrac{7}{12}$ ☐ $\dfrac{8}{11}$

7) $\dfrac{1}{3}$ ☐ $\dfrac{2}{8}$ 8) $\dfrac{1}{4}$ ☐ $\dfrac{6}{9}$ 9) $\dfrac{5}{8}$ ☐ $\dfrac{1}{6}$

10) $\dfrac{8}{9}$ ☐ $\dfrac{4}{7}$ 11) $\dfrac{5}{12}$ ☐ $\dfrac{9}{11}$ 12) $\dfrac{5}{7}$ ☐ $\dfrac{1}{4}$

13) $\dfrac{2}{12}$ ☐ $\dfrac{8}{9}$ 14) $\dfrac{7}{8}$ ☐ $\dfrac{1}{7}$ 15) $\dfrac{1}{6}$ ☐ $\dfrac{7}{9}$

16) $\dfrac{5}{6}$ ☐ $\dfrac{9}{12}$ 17) $\dfrac{1}{11}$ ☐ $\dfrac{5}{8}$ 18) $\dfrac{8}{20}$ ☐ $\dfrac{2}{5}$

19) $\dfrac{8}{11}$ ☐ $\dfrac{4}{8}$ 20) $\dfrac{5}{10}$ ☐ $\dfrac{4}{7}$ 21) $\dfrac{12}{16}$ ☐ $\dfrac{3}{4}$

Comparing Fractions

Compare the fractions and write the correct symbol (<, = or >) in each box.

1) $\dfrac{7}{8}$ ☐ $\dfrac{3}{10}$ 2) $\dfrac{2}{3}$ ☐ $\dfrac{3}{9}$ 3) $\dfrac{9}{12}$ ☐ $\dfrac{2}{4}$

4) $\dfrac{8}{11}$ ☐ $\dfrac{1}{3}$ 5) $\dfrac{1}{8}$ ☐ $\dfrac{8}{12}$ 6) $\dfrac{2}{4}$ ☐ $\dfrac{7}{8}$

7) $\dfrac{1}{3}$ ☐ $\dfrac{6}{12}$ 8) $\dfrac{1}{10}$ ☐ $\dfrac{8}{9}$ 9) $\dfrac{2}{3}$ ☐ $\dfrac{8}{10}$

10) $\dfrac{9}{11}$ ☐ $\dfrac{3}{6}$ 11) $\dfrac{8}{12}$ ☐ $\dfrac{4}{5}$ 12) $\dfrac{6}{10}$ ☐ $\dfrac{2}{9}$

13) $\dfrac{6}{9}$ ☐ $\dfrac{3}{8}$ 14) $\dfrac{3}{10}$ ☐ $\dfrac{5}{9}$ 15) $\dfrac{3}{9}$ ☐ $\dfrac{1}{10}$

16) $\dfrac{7}{11}$ ☐ $\dfrac{8}{12}$ 17) $\dfrac{1}{6}$ ☐ $\dfrac{8}{10}$ 18) $\dfrac{2}{7}$ ☐ $\dfrac{1}{4}$

19) $\dfrac{2}{7}$ ☐ $\dfrac{3}{4}$ 20) $\dfrac{6}{8}$ ☐ $\dfrac{2}{11}$ 21) $\dfrac{4}{9}$ ☐ $\dfrac{8}{12}$

Comparing Fractions

Compare the fractions and write the correct symbol (<, = or >) in each box.

1) $\dfrac{6}{7}$ ☐ $\dfrac{8}{9}$

2) $\dfrac{9}{12}$ ☐ $\dfrac{1}{7}$

3) $\dfrac{2}{11}$ ☐ $\dfrac{3}{10}$

4) $\dfrac{1}{8}$ ☐ $\dfrac{4}{5}$

5) $\dfrac{4}{10}$ ☐ $\dfrac{9}{12}$

6) $\dfrac{6}{8}$ ☐ $\dfrac{4}{9}$

7) $\dfrac{7}{12}$ ☐ $\dfrac{5}{6}$

8) $\dfrac{5}{8}$ ☐ $\dfrac{9}{10}$

9) $\dfrac{2}{7}$ ☐ $\dfrac{10}{35}$

10) $\dfrac{4}{10}$ ☐ $\dfrac{8}{9}$

11) $\dfrac{4}{11}$ ☐ $\dfrac{5}{8}$

12) $\dfrac{7}{9}$ ☐ $\dfrac{9}{11}$

13) $\dfrac{1}{11}$ ☐ $\dfrac{5}{8}$

14) $\dfrac{1}{2}$ ☐ $\dfrac{5}{9}$

15) $\dfrac{6}{11}$ ☐ $\dfrac{5}{6}$

16) $\dfrac{4}{5}$ ☐ $\dfrac{9}{12}$

17) $\dfrac{2}{9}$ ☐ $\dfrac{8}{36}$

18) $\dfrac{4}{7}$ ☐ $\dfrac{8}{10}$

19) $\dfrac{5}{6}$ ☐ $\dfrac{4}{9}$

20) $\dfrac{6}{7}$ ☐ $\dfrac{3}{5}$

21) $\dfrac{1}{3}$ ☐ $\dfrac{3}{7}$

Comparing Fractions

Compare the fractions and write the correct symbol (<, = or >) in each box.

1) $\dfrac{8}{10}$ ☐ $\dfrac{6}{8}$

2) $\dfrac{1}{7}$ ☐ $\dfrac{5}{11}$

3) $\dfrac{5}{8}$ ☐ $\dfrac{4}{7}$

4) $\dfrac{2}{11}$ ☐ $\dfrac{8}{44}$

5) $\dfrac{5}{12}$ ☐ $\dfrac{8}{10}$

6) $\dfrac{7}{9}$ ☐ $\dfrac{4}{11}$

7) $\dfrac{1}{7}$ ☐ $\dfrac{7}{8}$

8) $\dfrac{3}{10}$ ☐ $\dfrac{9}{11}$

9) $\dfrac{1}{6}$ ☐ $\dfrac{4}{8}$

10) $\dfrac{4}{12}$ ☐ $\dfrac{2}{10}$

11) $\dfrac{6}{8}$ ☐ $\dfrac{1}{12}$

12) $\dfrac{1}{7}$ ☐ $\dfrac{4}{10}$

13) $\dfrac{1}{10}$ ☐ $\dfrac{4}{7}$

14) $\dfrac{1}{7}$ ☐ $\dfrac{8}{10}$

15) $\dfrac{8}{12}$ ☐ $\dfrac{5}{11}$

16) $\dfrac{2}{11}$ ☐ $\dfrac{8}{12}$

17) $\dfrac{8}{9}$ ☐ $\dfrac{32}{36}$

18) $\dfrac{4}{5}$ ☐ $\dfrac{1}{7}$

19) $\dfrac{3}{5}$ ☐ $\dfrac{1}{9}$

20) $\dfrac{3}{11}$ ☐ $\dfrac{6}{22}$

21) $\dfrac{7}{8}$ ☐ $\dfrac{9}{12}$

Comparing Fractions

Compare the fractions and write the correct symbol (<, = or >) in each box.

1) $\dfrac{9}{10}$ ☐ $\dfrac{8}{11}$

2) $\dfrac{5}{9}$ ☐ $\dfrac{2}{7}$

3) $\dfrac{1}{6}$ ☐ $\dfrac{7}{12}$

4) $\dfrac{1}{5}$ ☐ $\dfrac{6}{12}$

5) $\dfrac{1}{8}$ ☐ $\dfrac{6}{10}$

6) $\dfrac{1}{11}$ ☐ $\dfrac{4}{6}$

7) $\dfrac{8}{10}$ ☐ $\dfrac{5}{6}$

8) $\dfrac{4}{5}$ ☐ $\dfrac{7}{12}$

9) $\dfrac{2}{8}$ ☐ $\dfrac{5}{11}$

10) $\dfrac{4}{8}$ ☐ $\dfrac{3}{11}$

11) $\dfrac{5}{10}$ ☐ $\dfrac{1}{4}$

12) $\dfrac{3}{5}$ ☐ $\dfrac{9}{15}$

13) $\dfrac{8}{12}$ ☐ $\dfrac{5}{7}$

14) $\dfrac{3}{8}$ ☐ $\dfrac{9}{12}$

15) $\dfrac{35}{40}$ ☐ $\dfrac{7}{8}$

16) $\dfrac{7}{10}$ ☐ $\dfrac{9}{11}$

17) $\dfrac{1}{7}$ ☐ $\dfrac{4}{5}$

18) $\dfrac{3}{11}$ ☐ $\dfrac{8}{10}$

19) $\dfrac{3}{12}$ ☐ $\dfrac{8}{9}$

20) $\dfrac{2}{22}$ ☐ $\dfrac{1}{11}$

21) $\dfrac{1}{8}$ ☐ $\dfrac{6}{7}$

Comparing Fractions

Compare the fractions and write the correct symbol (<, = or >) in each box.

1) $\dfrac{2}{7}$ ☐ $\dfrac{3}{12}$ 2) $\dfrac{2}{11}$ ☐ $\dfrac{6}{7}$ 3) $\dfrac{4}{7}$ ☐ $\dfrac{3}{10}$

4) $\dfrac{1}{4}$ ☐ $\dfrac{4}{5}$ 5) $\dfrac{7}{8}$ ☐ $\dfrac{1}{11}$ 6) $\dfrac{6}{11}$ ☐ $\dfrac{1}{4}$

7) $\dfrac{1}{6}$ ☐ $\dfrac{5}{9}$ 8) $\dfrac{6}{12}$ ☐ $\dfrac{3}{8}$ 9) $\dfrac{9}{10}$ ☐ $\dfrac{3}{12}$

10) $\dfrac{2}{4}$ ☐ $\dfrac{9}{10}$ 11) $\dfrac{49}{63}$ ☐ $\dfrac{7}{9}$ 12) $\dfrac{7}{9}$ ☐ $\dfrac{1}{4}$

13) $\dfrac{3}{10}$ ☐ $\dfrac{15}{50}$ 14) $\dfrac{1}{11}$ ☐ $\dfrac{7}{12}$ 15) $\dfrac{7}{12}$ ☐ $\dfrac{6}{11}$

16) $\dfrac{4}{6}$ ☐ $\dfrac{5}{8}$ 17) $\dfrac{3}{8}$ ☐ $\dfrac{9}{11}$ 18) $\dfrac{7}{11}$ ☐ $\dfrac{9}{10}$

19) $\dfrac{2}{10}$ ☐ $\dfrac{4}{9}$ 20) $\dfrac{3}{12}$ ☐ $\dfrac{1}{5}$ 21) $\dfrac{1}{8}$ ☐ $\dfrac{9}{12}$

Comparing Fractions

Compare the fractions and write the correct symbol (<, = or >) in each box.

1) $\dfrac{1}{11}$ ☐ $\dfrac{2}{10}$ 2) $\dfrac{4}{10}$ ☐ $\dfrac{3}{5}$ 3) $\dfrac{2}{11}$ ☐ $\dfrac{1}{3}$

4) $\dfrac{8}{9}$ ☐ $\dfrac{7}{11}$ 5) $\dfrac{5}{12}$ ☐ $\dfrac{3}{9}$ 6) $\dfrac{4}{6}$ ☐ $\dfrac{5}{8}$

7) $\dfrac{2}{6}$ ☐ $\dfrac{9}{12}$ 8) $\dfrac{5}{10}$ ☐ $\dfrac{6}{7}$ 9) $\dfrac{3}{9}$ ☐ $\dfrac{2}{10}$

10) $\dfrac{2}{12}$ ☐ $\dfrac{5}{9}$ 11) $\dfrac{1}{6}$ ☐ $\dfrac{6}{12}$ 12) $\dfrac{5}{11}$ ☐ $\dfrac{2}{3}$

13) $\dfrac{4}{6}$ ☐ $\dfrac{8}{10}$ 14) $\dfrac{8}{9}$ ☐ $\dfrac{24}{27}$ 15) $\dfrac{9}{12}$ ☐ $\dfrac{6}{8}$

16) $\dfrac{6}{9}$ ☐ $\dfrac{2}{3}$ 17) $\dfrac{3}{7}$ ☐ $\dfrac{1}{6}$ 18) $\dfrac{5}{11}$ ☐ $\dfrac{35}{77}$

19) $\dfrac{6}{11}$ ☐ $\dfrac{7}{10}$ 20) $\dfrac{1}{12}$ ☐ $\dfrac{3}{8}$ 21) $\dfrac{3}{7}$ ☐ $\dfrac{2}{9}$

www.claymaze.com

Comparing Fractions

Compare the fractions and write the correct symbol (<, = or >) in each box.

1) $\dfrac{3}{12}$ ☐ $\dfrac{1}{9}$ 2) $\dfrac{5}{8}$ ☐ $\dfrac{9}{11}$ 3) $\dfrac{16}{48}$ ☐ $\dfrac{4}{12}$

4) $\dfrac{3}{10}$ ☐ $\dfrac{5}{6}$ 5) $\dfrac{1}{5}$ ☐ $\dfrac{5}{7}$ 6) $\dfrac{7}{10}$ ☐ $\dfrac{1}{8}$

7) $\dfrac{3}{11}$ ☐ $\dfrac{9}{10}$ 8) $\dfrac{4}{10}$ ☐ $\dfrac{8}{9}$ 9) $\dfrac{15}{60}$ ☐ $\dfrac{3}{12}$

10) $\dfrac{4}{8}$ ☐ $\dfrac{1}{4}$ 11) $\dfrac{2}{12}$ ☐ $\dfrac{3}{8}$ 12) $\dfrac{3}{6}$ ☐ $\dfrac{9}{11}$

13) $\dfrac{5}{6}$ ☐ $\dfrac{35}{42}$ 14) $\dfrac{4}{16}$ ☐ $\dfrac{1}{4}$ 15) $\dfrac{8}{12}$ ☐ $\dfrac{1}{7}$

16) $\dfrac{1}{9}$ ☐ $\dfrac{5}{7}$ 17) $\dfrac{5}{11}$ ☐ $\dfrac{8}{9}$ 18) $\dfrac{7}{10}$ ☐ $\dfrac{4}{8}$

19) $\dfrac{2}{5}$ ☐ $\dfrac{9}{12}$ 20) $\dfrac{18}{21}$ ☐ $\dfrac{6}{7}$ 21) $\dfrac{1}{9}$ ☐ $\dfrac{9}{10}$

Comparing Fractions

Compare the fractions and write the correct symbol (<, = or >) in each box.

1) $\dfrac{7}{8}$ $\square$ $\dfrac{8}{12}$ 2) $\dfrac{2}{10}$ $\square$ $\dfrac{3}{6}$ 3) $\dfrac{5}{6}$ $\square$ $\dfrac{9}{12}$

4) $\dfrac{8}{10}$ $\square$ $\dfrac{6}{7}$ 5) $\dfrac{5}{8}$ $\square$ $\dfrac{3}{4}$ 6) $\dfrac{7}{10}$ $\square$ $\dfrac{8}{11}$

7) $\dfrac{2}{7}$ $\square$ $\dfrac{9}{11}$ 8) $\dfrac{5}{10}$ $\square$ $\dfrac{4}{9}$ 9) $\dfrac{1}{9}$ $\square$ $\dfrac{7}{10}$

10) $\dfrac{4}{10}$ $\square$ $\dfrac{6}{8}$ 11) $\dfrac{1}{2}$ $\square$ $\dfrac{5}{11}$ 12) $\dfrac{4}{8}$ $\square$ $\dfrac{28}{56}$

13) $\dfrac{5}{11}$ $\square$ $\dfrac{8}{10}$ 14) $\dfrac{8}{9}$ $\square$ $\dfrac{6}{12}$ 15) $\dfrac{4}{11}$ $\square$ $\dfrac{1}{10}$

16) $\dfrac{12}{14}$ $\square$ $\dfrac{6}{7}$ 17) $\dfrac{6}{12}$ $\square$ $\dfrac{2}{8}$ 18) $\dfrac{8}{10}$ $\square$ $\dfrac{1}{2}$

19) $\dfrac{5}{9}$ $\square$ $\dfrac{9}{12}$ 20) $\dfrac{8}{11}$ $\square$ $\dfrac{32}{44}$ 21) $\dfrac{2}{4}$ $\square$ $\dfrac{1}{8}$

Name _____   Date _____

Comparing Fractions

Compare the fractions and write the correct symbol (<, = or >) in each box.

1) $\dfrac{2}{5}$ ☐ $\dfrac{4}{10}$ 　　2) $\dfrac{3}{6}$ ☐ $\dfrac{1}{8}$ 　　3) $\dfrac{4}{12}$ ☐ $\dfrac{2}{4}$

4) $\dfrac{1}{2}$ ☐ $\dfrac{5}{9}$ 　　5) $\dfrac{9}{11}$ ☐ $\dfrac{2}{10}$ 　　6) $\dfrac{5}{9}$ ☐ $\dfrac{3}{5}$

7) $\dfrac{4}{8}$ ☐ $\dfrac{6}{7}$ 　　8) $\dfrac{3}{12}$ ☐ $\dfrac{8}{9}$ 　　9) $\dfrac{7}{10}$ ☐ $\dfrac{9}{11}$

10) $\dfrac{1}{3}$ ☐ $\dfrac{2}{10}$ 　　11) $\dfrac{7}{10}$ ☐ $\dfrac{8}{11}$ 　　12) $\dfrac{5}{6}$ ☐ $\dfrac{2}{8}$

13) $\dfrac{7}{9}$ ☐ $\dfrac{6}{11}$ 　　14) $\dfrac{7}{11}$ ☐ $\dfrac{9}{12}$ 　　15) $\dfrac{56}{70}$ ☐ $\dfrac{8}{10}$

16) $\dfrac{7}{11}$ ☐ $\dfrac{4}{7}$ 　　17) $\dfrac{2}{8}$ ☐ $\dfrac{7}{10}$ 　　18) $\dfrac{7}{12}$ ☐ $\dfrac{1}{2}$

19) $\dfrac{2}{8}$ ☐ $\dfrac{9}{10}$ 　　20) $\dfrac{8}{9}$ ☐ $\dfrac{5}{12}$ 　　21) $\dfrac{1}{3}$ ☐ $\dfrac{9}{11}$

SECTION

FRACTION ADDITION AND SUBTRACTION

11 worksheets
8 problems per sheet

Fraction Addition and Subtraction

Add the fractions and simplify.

1) $\dfrac{1}{10} + \dfrac{5}{8} =$ _____

2) $\dfrac{4}{7} + \dfrac{8}{11} =$ _____

3) $\dfrac{3}{8} + \dfrac{3}{7} =$ _____

4) $\dfrac{9}{12} + \dfrac{5}{6} =$ _____

Subtract the fractions and simplify.

5) $\dfrac{6}{8} - \dfrac{6}{11} =$ _____

6) $\dfrac{9}{12} - \dfrac{4}{7} =$ _____

7) $\dfrac{7}{8} - \dfrac{3}{5} =$ _____

8) $\dfrac{7}{9} - \dfrac{5}{7} =$ _____

Fraction Addition and Subtraction

Add the fractions and simplify.

1) $\dfrac{9}{11} + \dfrac{7}{8} =$ _____

2) $\dfrac{2}{9} + \dfrac{1}{5} =$ _____

3) $\dfrac{4}{12} + \dfrac{5}{7} =$ _____

4) $\dfrac{7}{11} + \dfrac{9}{12} =$ _____

Subtract the fractions and simplify.

5) $\dfrac{8}{10} - \dfrac{5}{11} =$ _____

6) $\dfrac{9}{12} - \dfrac{1}{10} =$ _____

7) $\dfrac{3}{4} - \dfrac{5}{8} =$ _____

8) $\dfrac{6}{9} - \dfrac{4}{10} =$ _____

Fraction Addition and Subtraction

Add the fractions and simplify.

1) $\dfrac{1}{4} + \dfrac{9}{11} =$ _____

2) $\dfrac{2}{5} + \dfrac{9}{10} =$ _____

3) $\dfrac{5}{7} + \dfrac{1}{8} =$ _____

4) $\dfrac{2}{12} + \dfrac{8}{11} =$ _____

Subtract the fractions and simplify.

5) $\dfrac{9}{10} - \dfrac{4}{7} =$ _____

6) $\dfrac{8}{9} - \dfrac{5}{11} =$ _____

7) $\dfrac{8}{12} - \dfrac{4}{9} =$ _____

8) $\dfrac{2}{5} - \dfrac{1}{11} =$ _____

Fraction Addition and Subtraction

Add the fractions and simplify.

1) $\dfrac{2}{10} + \dfrac{6}{8} =$ _____

2) $\dfrac{1}{2} + \dfrac{8}{10} =$ _____

3) $\dfrac{5}{9} + \dfrac{5}{6} =$ _____

4) $\dfrac{5}{8} + \dfrac{3}{10} =$ _____

Subtract the fractions and simplify.

5) $\dfrac{9}{10} - \dfrac{9}{11} =$ _____

6) $\dfrac{6}{8} - \dfrac{1}{3} =$ _____

7) $\dfrac{1}{6} - \dfrac{1}{8} =$ _____

8) $\dfrac{6}{7} - \dfrac{3}{11} =$ _____

Fraction Addition and Subtraction

Add the fractions and simplify.

1) $\dfrac{6}{11} + \dfrac{8}{10} =$ _____

2) $\dfrac{5}{9} + \dfrac{3}{8} =$ _____

3) $\dfrac{7}{12} + \dfrac{3}{4} =$ _____

4) $\dfrac{9}{11} + \dfrac{5}{9} =$ _____

Subtract the fractions and simplify.

5) $\dfrac{8}{9} - \dfrac{3}{10} =$ _____

6) $\dfrac{5}{7} - \dfrac{1}{12} =$ _____

7) $\dfrac{7}{8} - \dfrac{8}{11} =$ _____

8) $\dfrac{4}{5} - \dfrac{5}{12} =$ _____

Fraction Addition and Subtraction

Add the fractions and simplify.

1) $\dfrac{6}{7} + \dfrac{2}{12} =$ _____

2) $\dfrac{3}{8} + \dfrac{3}{10} =$ _____

3) $\dfrac{2}{9} + \dfrac{3}{12} =$ _____

4) $\dfrac{9}{11} + \dfrac{5}{7} =$ _____

Subtract the fractions and simplify.

5) $\dfrac{5}{6} - \dfrac{2}{5} =$ _____

6) $\dfrac{9}{10} - \dfrac{7}{11} =$ _____

7) $\dfrac{7}{8} - \dfrac{5}{9} =$ _____

8) $\dfrac{8}{11} - \dfrac{1}{7} =$ _____

Fraction Addition and Subtraction

Add the fractions and simplify.

1) $\dfrac{6}{8} + \dfrac{3}{10} =$ _____

2) $\dfrac{4}{12} + \dfrac{5}{8} =$ _____

3) $\dfrac{5}{11} + \dfrac{6}{7} =$ _____

4) $\dfrac{5}{6} + \dfrac{2}{5} =$ _____

Subtract the fractions and simplify.

5) $\dfrac{9}{12} - \dfrac{5}{10} =$ _____

6) $\dfrac{7}{8} - \dfrac{9}{12} =$ _____

7) $\dfrac{9}{11} - \dfrac{8}{10} =$ _____

8) $\dfrac{8}{9} - \dfrac{3}{8} =$ _____

Fraction Addition and Subtraction

Add the fractions and simplify.

1) $\dfrac{7}{12} + \dfrac{3}{8} =$ _____

2) $\dfrac{2}{7} + \dfrac{7}{12} =$ _____

3) $\dfrac{5}{12} + \dfrac{7}{9} =$ _____

4) $\dfrac{8}{9} + \dfrac{1}{3} =$ _____

Subtract the fractions and simplify.

5) $\dfrac{9}{10} - \dfrac{1}{2} =$ _____

6) $\dfrac{3}{11} - \dfrac{1}{4} =$ _____

7) $\dfrac{9}{12} - \dfrac{3}{9} =$ _____

8) $\dfrac{6}{7} - \dfrac{6}{10} =$ _____

Fraction Addition and Subtraction

Add the fractions and simplify.

1) $\dfrac{6}{7} + \dfrac{9}{10} =$ _____

2) $\dfrac{8}{11} + \dfrac{2}{8} =$ _____

3) $\dfrac{3}{10} + \dfrac{5}{7} =$ _____

4) $\dfrac{4}{11} + \dfrac{7}{9} =$ _____

Subtract the fractions and simplify.

5) $\dfrac{2}{3} - \dfrac{1}{6} =$ _____

6) $\dfrac{3}{8} - \dfrac{2}{10} =$ _____

7) $\dfrac{9}{12} - \dfrac{2}{11} =$ _____

8) $\dfrac{8}{9} - \dfrac{8}{10} =$ _____

Name _____   Date _____

Fraction Addition and Subtraction

Add the fractions and simplify.

1) $\frac{4}{9} + \frac{3}{5} =$ _____

2) $\frac{1}{5} + \frac{7}{10} =$ _____

3) $\frac{1}{12} + \frac{2}{5} =$ _____

4) $\frac{6}{9} + \frac{1}{8} =$ _____

Subtract the fractions and simplify.

5) $\frac{3}{4} - \frac{4}{10} =$ _____

6) $\frac{2}{3} - \frac{5}{9} =$ _____

7) $\frac{9}{11} - \frac{4}{5} =$ _____

8) $\frac{9}{10} - \frac{5}{9} =$ _____

Fraction Addition and Subtraction

Add the fractions and simplify.

1) $\dfrac{9}{10} + \dfrac{2}{3} =$ _____

2) $\dfrac{7}{12} + \dfrac{3}{7} =$ _____

3) $\dfrac{4}{7} + \dfrac{1}{6} =$ _____

4) $\dfrac{4}{10} + \dfrac{7}{8} =$ _____

Subtract the fractions and simplify.

5) $\dfrac{7}{9} - \dfrac{3}{4} =$ _____

6) $\dfrac{9}{11} - \dfrac{4}{7} =$ _____

7) $\dfrac{1}{3} - \dfrac{3}{11} =$ _____

8) $\dfrac{3}{5} - \dfrac{2}{12} =$ _____

SECTION

7

FRACTION MULTIPLICATION AND DIVISION

11 worksheets
8 problems per sheet

Fraction Multiplication and Division

Multiply the fractions and simplify.

1) $\dfrac{4}{11} \times \dfrac{2}{5} =$ _____

2) $\dfrac{6}{8} \times \dfrac{4}{9} =$ _____

3) $\dfrac{2}{4} \times \dfrac{4}{11} =$ _____

4) $\dfrac{5}{9} \times \dfrac{5}{6} =$ _____

Divide the fractions and simplify.

5) $\dfrac{6}{11} \div \dfrac{6}{12} =$ _____

6) $\dfrac{5}{6} \div \dfrac{1}{5} =$ _____

7) $\dfrac{7}{10} \div \dfrac{3}{12} =$ _____

8) $\dfrac{5}{12} \div \dfrac{4}{10} =$ _____

Fraction Multiplication and Division

Multiply the fractions and simplify.

1) $\dfrac{2}{7}$ x $\dfrac{7}{9}$ = _____

2) $\dfrac{7}{9}$ x $\dfrac{2}{4}$ = _____

3) $\dfrac{2}{11}$ x $\dfrac{5}{7}$ = _____

4) $\dfrac{4}{8}$ x $\dfrac{2}{10}$ = _____

Divide the fractions and simplify.

5) $\dfrac{2}{4}$ ÷ $\dfrac{4}{11}$ = _____

6) $\dfrac{5}{6}$ ÷ $\dfrac{3}{4}$ = _____

7) $\dfrac{4}{10}$ ÷ $\dfrac{3}{8}$ = _____

8) $\dfrac{7}{10}$ ÷ $\dfrac{2}{5}$ = _____

Fraction Multiplication and Division

Multiply the fractions and simplify.

1) $\dfrac{1}{9} \times \dfrac{2}{3} =$ _____

2) $\dfrac{6}{8} \times \dfrac{5}{6} =$ _____

3) $\dfrac{8}{11} \times \dfrac{2}{10} =$ _____

4) $\dfrac{1}{6} \times \dfrac{6}{9} =$ _____

Divide the fractions and simplify.

5) $\dfrac{8}{9} \div \dfrac{9}{11} =$ _____

6) $\dfrac{3}{4} \div \dfrac{3}{6} =$ _____

7) $\dfrac{8}{9} \div \dfrac{7}{8} =$ _____

8) $\dfrac{6}{8} \div \dfrac{5}{10} =$ _____

Fraction Multiplication and Division

Multiply the fractions and simplify.

1) $\dfrac{1}{7} \times \dfrac{7}{9} =$ _____

2) $\dfrac{5}{6} \times \dfrac{7}{10} =$ _____

3) $\dfrac{9}{10} \times \dfrac{1}{7} =$ _____

4) $\dfrac{6}{12} \times \dfrac{8}{10} =$ _____

Divide the fractions and simplify.

5) $\dfrac{4}{6} \div \dfrac{4}{7} =$ _____

6) $\dfrac{6}{10} \div \dfrac{5}{9} =$ _____

7) $\dfrac{5}{8} \div \dfrac{6}{12} =$ _____

8) $\dfrac{7}{12} \div \dfrac{2}{7} =$ _____

Fraction Multiplication and Division

Multiply the fractions and simplify.

1) $\dfrac{6}{12} \times \dfrac{8}{10} =$ _____

2) $\dfrac{3}{6} \times \dfrac{3}{9} =$ _____

3) $\dfrac{7}{12} \times \dfrac{7}{10} =$ _____

4) $\dfrac{1}{11} \times \dfrac{3}{8} =$ _____

Divide the fractions and simplify.

5) $\dfrac{6}{7} \div \dfrac{3}{12} =$ _____

6) $\dfrac{6}{11} \div \dfrac{2}{10} =$ _____

7) $\dfrac{9}{12} \div \dfrac{2}{3} =$ _____

8) $\dfrac{2}{3} \div \dfrac{7}{11} =$ _____

Fraction Multiplication and Division

Multiply the fractions and simplify.

1) $\dfrac{1}{6} \times \dfrac{8}{9} =$ _____

2) $\dfrac{4}{12} \times \dfrac{2}{5} =$ _____

3) $\dfrac{8}{11} \times \dfrac{7}{12} =$ _____

4) $\dfrac{1}{8} \times \dfrac{5}{11} =$ _____

Divide the fractions and simplify.

5) $\dfrac{7}{12} \div \dfrac{1}{3} =$ _____

6) $\dfrac{5}{7} \div \dfrac{7}{10} =$ _____

7) $\dfrac{7}{10} \div \dfrac{4}{9} =$ _____

8) $\dfrac{7}{12} \div \dfrac{1}{7} =$ _____

Fraction Multiplication and Division

Multiply the fractions and simplify.

1) $\dfrac{9}{11} \times \dfrac{3}{6} =$ _____

2) $\dfrac{1}{10} \times \dfrac{1}{4} =$ _____

3) $\dfrac{6}{7} \times \dfrac{8}{9} =$ _____

4) $\dfrac{7}{11} \times \dfrac{2}{12} =$ _____

Divide the fractions and simplify.

5) $\dfrac{7}{10} \div \dfrac{1}{5} =$ _____

6) $\dfrac{7}{9} \div \dfrac{3}{8} =$ _____

7) $\dfrac{2}{5} \div \dfrac{1}{11} =$ _____

8) $\dfrac{8}{11} \div \dfrac{4}{12} =$ _____

Fraction Multiplication and Division

Multiply the fractions and simplify.

1) $\dfrac{5}{10} \times \dfrac{7}{9} =$ _____

2) $\dfrac{6}{7} \times \dfrac{6}{12} =$ _____

3) $\dfrac{2}{3} \times \dfrac{8}{11} =$ _____

4) $\dfrac{1}{6} \times \dfrac{3}{10} =$ _____

Divide the fractions and simplify.

5) $\dfrac{5}{7} \div \dfrac{3}{11} =$ _____

6) $\dfrac{9}{11} \div \dfrac{7}{12} =$ _____

7) $\dfrac{6}{12} \div \dfrac{4}{11} =$ _____

8) $\dfrac{2}{7} \div \dfrac{1}{8} =$ _____

Fraction Multiplication and Division

Multiply the fractions and simplify.

1) $\dfrac{1}{5} \times \dfrac{7}{11} =$ _____

2) $\dfrac{9}{11} \times \dfrac{5}{8} =$ _____

3) $\dfrac{7}{8} \times \dfrac{5}{9} =$ _____

4) $\dfrac{9}{10} \times \dfrac{4}{7} =$ _____

Divide the fractions and simplify.

5) $\dfrac{7}{11} \div \dfrac{3}{12} =$ _____

6) $\dfrac{9}{10} \div \dfrac{1}{5} =$ _____

7) $\dfrac{4}{8} \div \dfrac{3}{7} =$ _____

8) $\dfrac{8}{11} \div \dfrac{4}{6} =$ _____

www.claymaze.com

Fraction Multiplication and Division

Multiply the fractions and simplify.

1) $\dfrac{8}{11} \times \dfrac{3}{6} =$ _____

2) $\dfrac{6}{9} \times \dfrac{1}{11} =$ _____

3) $\dfrac{7}{11} \times \dfrac{2}{7} =$ _____

4) $\dfrac{4}{7} \times \dfrac{8}{10} =$ _____

Divide the fractions and simplify.

5) $\dfrac{6}{10} \div \dfrac{4}{7} =$ _____

6) $\dfrac{7}{9} \div \dfrac{1}{11} =$ _____

7) $\dfrac{6}{7} \div \dfrac{6}{9} =$ _____

8) $\dfrac{6}{10} \div \dfrac{1}{3} =$ _____

Fraction Multiplication and Division

Multiply the fractions and simplify.

1) $\dfrac{4}{5} \times \dfrac{3}{11} =$ _____

2) $\dfrac{6}{12} \times \dfrac{1}{4} =$ _____

3) $\dfrac{5}{10} \times \dfrac{2}{3} =$ _____

4) $\dfrac{2}{3} \times \dfrac{1}{6} =$ _____

Divide the fractions and simplify.

5) $\dfrac{3}{5} \div \dfrac{5}{9} =$ _____

6) $\dfrac{7}{8} \div \dfrac{3}{4} =$ _____

7) $\dfrac{8}{11} \div \dfrac{8}{12} =$ _____

8) $\dfrac{4}{6} \div \dfrac{4}{7} =$ _____

SECTION

CONVERTING FRACTIONS & DECIMALS

11 worksheets
24 problems per sheet

Converting Fractions & Decimals | 10ths, 100ths & 1000ths

Convert the fractions to decimals.

1) $\dfrac{6}{10}$ = _____

2) $\dfrac{265}{1000}$ = _____

3) $\dfrac{4}{100}$ = _____

4) $\dfrac{50}{100}$ = _____

5) $\dfrac{2}{100}$ = _____

6) $\dfrac{3}{10}$ = _____

7) $\dfrac{8}{1000}$ = _____

8) $\dfrac{198}{1000}$ = _____

9) $\dfrac{28}{100}$ = _____

10) $\dfrac{2}{10}$ = _____

11) $\dfrac{46}{1000}$ = _____

12) $\dfrac{122}{1000}$ = _____

Convert the decimals to fractions. Write as 10ths, 100ths or 1000ths.

13) .029 = _____

14) .9 = _____

15) .01 = _____

16) .24 = _____

17) .44 = _____

18) .04 = _____

19) .69 = _____

20) .536 = _____

21) .631 = _____

22) .4 = _____

23) .54 = _____

24) .47 = _____

Converting Fractions & Decimals   10ths, 100ths & 1000ths

Convert the fractions to decimals.

1) $\dfrac{76}{1000}$ = _____

2) $\dfrac{846}{1000}$ = _____

3) $\dfrac{45}{100}$ = _____

4) $\dfrac{5}{10}$ = _____

5) $\dfrac{40}{100}$ = _____

6) $\dfrac{41}{1000}$ = _____

7) $\dfrac{1}{10}$ = _____

8) $\dfrac{12}{100}$ = _____

9) $\dfrac{89}{100}$ = _____

10) $\dfrac{517}{1000}$ = _____

11) $\dfrac{3}{100}$ = _____

12) $\dfrac{38}{100}$ = _____

Convert the decimals to fractions. Write as 10ths, 100ths or 1000ths.

13) .16 = _____

14) .09 = _____

15) .2 = _____

16) .094 = _____

17) .7 = _____

18) .537 = _____

19) .19 = _____

20) .6 = _____

21) .017 = _____

22) .85 = _____

23) .1 = _____

24) .04 = _____

Converting Fractions & Decimals   10ths, 100ths & 1000ths

Convert the fractions to decimals.

1) $\dfrac{7}{10}$ = _____

2) $\dfrac{1}{10}$ = _____

3) $\dfrac{5}{100}$ = _____

4) $\dfrac{2}{100}$ = _____

5) $\dfrac{8}{100}$ = _____

6) $\dfrac{1}{100}$ = _____

7) $\dfrac{3}{10}$ = _____

8) $\dfrac{5}{10}$ = _____

9) $\dfrac{71}{1000}$ = _____

10) $\dfrac{9}{10}$ = _____

11) $\dfrac{6}{10}$ = _____

12) $\dfrac{4}{100}$ = _____

Convert the decimals to fractions. Write as 10ths, 100ths or 1000ths.

13) .5 = _____

14) .672 = _____

15) .007 = _____

16) .246 = _____

17) .7 = _____

18) .017 = _____

19) .55 = _____

20) .004 = _____

21) .2 = _____

22) .079 = _____

23) .024 = _____

24) .6 = _____

www.claymaze.com

Converting Fractions & Decimals   10ths, 100ths & 1000ths

Convert the fractions to decimals.

1) $\dfrac{8}{100}$ = _____

2) $\dfrac{67}{1000}$ = _____

3) $\dfrac{65}{100}$ = _____

4) $\dfrac{85}{100}$ = _____

5) $\dfrac{6}{10}$ = _____

6) $\dfrac{889}{1000}$ = _____

7) $\dfrac{74}{100}$ = _____

8) $\dfrac{3}{10}$ = _____

9) $\dfrac{84}{1000}$ = _____

10) $\dfrac{37}{100}$ = _____

11) $\dfrac{7}{100}$ = _____

12) $\dfrac{764}{1000}$ = _____

Convert the decimals to fractions. Write as 10ths, 100ths or 1000ths.

13) .7 = _____

14) .2 = _____

15) .071 = _____

16) .65 = _____

17) .236 = _____

18) .095 = _____

19) .792 = _____

20) .518 = _____

21) .5 = _____

22) .198 = _____

23) .8 = _____

24) .001 = _____

www.claymaze.com

Converting Fractions & Decimals   10ths, 100ths & 1000ths

Convert the fractions to decimals.

1) $\dfrac{2}{10}$ = _____

2) $\dfrac{49}{100}$ = _____

3) $\dfrac{82}{1000}$ = _____

4) $\dfrac{82}{100}$ = _____

5) $\dfrac{98}{1000}$ = _____

6) $\dfrac{40}{1000}$ = _____

7) $\dfrac{58}{100}$ = _____

8) $\dfrac{26}{100}$ = _____

9) $\dfrac{83}{100}$ = _____

10) $\dfrac{93}{100}$ = _____

11) $\dfrac{631}{1000}$ = _____

12) $\dfrac{84}{100}$ = _____

Convert the decimals to fractions. Write as 10ths, 100ths or 1000ths.

13) .632 = _____

14) .1 = _____

15) .07 = _____

16) .3 = _____

17) .54 = _____

18) .99 = _____

19) .4 = _____

20) .011 = _____

21) .61 = _____

22) .086 = _____

23) .001 = _____

24) .2 = _____

Converting Fractions & Decimals | 10ths, 100ths & 1000ths

Convert the fractions to decimals.

1) $\dfrac{13}{100}$ = _____

2) $\dfrac{41}{100}$ = _____

3) $\dfrac{54}{1000}$ = _____

4) $\dfrac{9}{100}$ = _____

5) $\dfrac{3}{10}$ = _____

6) $\dfrac{47}{100}$ = _____

7) $\dfrac{6}{10}$ = _____

8) $\dfrac{533}{1000}$ = _____

9) $\dfrac{98}{100}$ = _____

10) $\dfrac{5}{10}$ = _____

11) $\dfrac{51}{100}$ = _____

12) $\dfrac{10}{1000}$ = _____

Convert the decimals to fractions. Write as 10ths, 100ths or 1000ths.

13) .05 = _____

14) .966 = _____

15) .3 = _____

16) .01 = _____

17) .48 = _____

18) .6 = _____

19) .337 = _____

20) .77 = _____

21) .287 = _____

22) .7 = _____

23) .64 = _____

24) .58 = _____

Converting Fractions & Decimals | 10ths, 100ths & 1000ths

Convert the fractions to decimals.

1) $\dfrac{82}{1000}$ = _____

2) $\dfrac{704}{1000}$ = _____

3) $\dfrac{1}{10}$ = _____

4) $\dfrac{8}{100}$ = _____

5) $\dfrac{80}{100}$ = _____

6) $\dfrac{251}{1000}$ = _____

7) $\dfrac{714}{1000}$ = _____

8) $\dfrac{8}{10}$ = _____

9) $\dfrac{2}{10}$ = _____

10) $\dfrac{4}{10}$ = _____

11) $\dfrac{56}{1000}$ = _____

12) $\dfrac{74}{100}$ = _____

Convert the decimals to fractions. Write as 10ths, 100ths or 1000ths.

13) .492 = _____

14) .5 = _____

15) .03 = _____

16) .4 = _____

17) .9 = _____

18) .11 = _____

19) .31 = _____

20) .701 = _____

21) .659 = _____

22) .2 = _____

23) .7 = _____

24) .68 = _____

Converting Fractions & Decimals | 10ths, 100ths & 1000ths

Convert the fractions to decimals.

1) $\dfrac{2}{100}$ = _____

2) $\dfrac{870}{1000}$ = _____

3) $\dfrac{2}{10}$ = _____

4) $\dfrac{4}{1000}$ = _____

5) $\dfrac{8}{10}$ = _____

6) $\dfrac{6}{100}$ = _____

7) $\dfrac{7}{10}$ = _____

8) $\dfrac{43}{1000}$ = _____

9) $\dfrac{531}{1000}$ = _____

10) $\dfrac{300}{1000}$ = _____

11) $\dfrac{1}{10}$ = _____

12) $\dfrac{4}{10}$ = _____

Convert the decimals to fractions. Write as 10ths, 100ths or 1000ths.

13) .23 = _____

14) .6 = _____

15) .7 = _____

16) .077 = _____

17) .3 = _____

18) .083 = _____

19) .63 = _____

20) .627 = _____

21) .9 = _____

22) .5 = _____

23) .8 = _____

24) .67 = _____

Converting Fractions & Decimals   10ths, 100ths & 1000ths

Convert the fractions to decimals.

1) $\dfrac{9}{10}$ = _____

2) $\dfrac{3}{1000}$ = _____

3) $\dfrac{8}{10}$ = _____

4) $\dfrac{6}{10}$ = _____

5) $\dfrac{2}{1000}$ = _____

6) $\dfrac{5}{10}$ = _____

7) $\dfrac{198}{1000}$ = _____

8) $\dfrac{366}{1000}$ = _____

9) $\dfrac{81}{1000}$ = _____

10) $\dfrac{4}{10}$ = _____

11) $\dfrac{81}{100}$ = _____

12) $\dfrac{82}{1000}$ = _____

Convert the decimals to fractions. Write as 10ths, 100ths or 1000ths.

13) $.389$ = _____

14) $.7$ = _____

15) $.142$ = _____

16) $.46$ = _____

17) $.052$ = _____

18) $.076$ = _____

19) $.273$ = _____

20) $.8$ = _____

21) $.9$ = _____

22) $.2$ = _____

23) $.24$ = _____

24) $.58$ = _____

Converting Fractions & Decimals — 10ths, 100ths & 1000ths

Convert the fractions to decimals.

1) $\dfrac{4}{10}$ = _____

2) $\dfrac{59}{100}$ = _____

3) $\dfrac{7}{10}$ = _____

4) $\dfrac{45}{100}$ = _____

5) $\dfrac{12}{100}$ = _____

6) $\dfrac{1}{10}$ = _____

7) $\dfrac{5}{100}$ = _____

8) $\dfrac{3}{10}$ = _____

9) $\dfrac{19}{100}$ = _____

10) $\dfrac{7}{100}$ = _____

11) $\dfrac{77}{100}$ = _____

12) $\dfrac{266}{1000}$ = _____

Convert the decimals to fractions. Write as 10ths, 100ths or 1000ths.

13) .698 = _____

14) .3 = _____

15) .006 = _____

16) .9 = _____

17) .493 = _____

18) .153 = _____

19) .06 = _____

20) .01 = _____

21) .37 = _____

22) .49 = _____

23) .848 = _____

24) .459 = _____

Converting Fractions & Decimals 10ths, 100ths & 1000ths

Convert the fractions to decimals.

1) $\dfrac{380}{1000} =$ _____

2) $\dfrac{7}{10} =$ _____

3) $\dfrac{4}{10} =$ _____

4) $\dfrac{69}{100} =$ _____

5) $\dfrac{2}{10} =$ _____

6) $\dfrac{8}{10} =$ _____

7) $\dfrac{35}{100} =$ _____

8) $\dfrac{62}{1000} =$ _____

9) $\dfrac{5}{10} =$ _____

10) $\dfrac{1}{10} =$ _____

11) $\dfrac{57}{100} =$ _____

12) $\dfrac{763}{1000} =$ _____

Convert the decimals to fractions. Write as 10ths, 100ths or 1000ths.

13) $.6 =$ _____

14) $.021 =$ _____

15) $.902 =$ _____

16) $.8 =$ _____

17) $.1 =$ _____

18) $.031 =$ _____

19) $.07 =$ _____

20) $.4 =$ _____

21) $.01 =$ _____

22) $.974 =$ _____

23) $.853 =$ _____

24) $.2 =$ _____

www.claymaze.com

SECTION

MULTIPLYING BY .1, .01 & .001

11 worksheets
24 problems per sheet

Multiplying by .1, .01 and .001

Multiply.

1) 62 x .001 = _____

2) 426 x .1 = _____

3) 705 x .001 = _____

4) 55 x .1 = _____

5) 81 x .001 = _____

6) 63 x .001 = _____

7) 95 x .1 = _____

8) 844 x .001 = _____

9) 475 x .1 = _____

10) 364 x .01 = _____

11) 88 x .1 = _____

12) 445 x .001 = _____

Fill in the blanks with .1, .01 or .001 to make the statements correct.

13) 476 x _____ = 4.76

14) 407 x _____ = 4.07

15) 66 x _____ = .066

16) 990 x _____ = .99

17) 881 x _____ = .881

18) 428 x _____ = 4.28

19) 64 x _____ = 6.4

20) 180 x _____ = 1.8

21) 123 x _____ = 1.23

22) 76 x _____ = .076

23) 175 x _____ = 17.5

24) 185 x _____ = 1.85

Multiplying by .1, .01 and .001

Multiply.

1) $57 \times .001 =$ _____

2) $194 \times .01 =$ _____

3) $13 \times .1 =$ _____

4) $261 \times .001 =$ _____

5) $967 \times .001 =$ _____

6) $845 \times .001 =$ _____

7) $482 \times .1 =$ _____

8) $636 \times .001 =$ _____

9) $988 \times .001 =$ _____

10) $50 \times .1 =$ _____

11) $872 \times .1 =$ _____

12) $56 \times .001 =$ _____

Fill in the blanks with .1, .01 or .001 to make the statements correct.

13) $16 \times$ _____ $= .16$

14) $192 \times$ _____ $= .192$

15) $56 \times$ _____ $= .56$

16) $624 \times$ _____ $= 6.24$

17) $318 \times$ _____ $= 3.18$

18) $254 \times$ _____ $= .254$

19) $511 \times$ _____ $= 5.11$

20) $662 \times$ _____ $= 66.2$

21) $42 \times$ _____ $= 4.2$

22) $809 \times$ _____ $= 8.09$

23) $824 \times$ _____ $= 8.24$

24) $75 \times$ _____ $= .075$

Multiplying by .1, .01 and .001

Multiply.

1) $312 \times .01 =$ _____

2) $405 \times .001 =$ _____

3) $100 \times .1 =$ _____

4) $386 \times .01 =$ _____

5) $172 \times .01 =$ _____

6) $375 \times .1 =$ _____

7) $939 \times .01 =$ _____

8) $96 \times .001 =$ _____

9) $21 \times .01 =$ _____

10) $685 \times .1 =$ _____

11) $860 \times .1 =$ _____

12) $672 \times .001 =$ _____

Fill in the blanks with .1, .01 or .001 to make the statements correct.

13) $22 \times$ _____ $= .22$

14) $74 \times$ _____ $= 7.4$

15) $29 \times$ _____ $= .029$

16) $67 \times$ _____ $= 6.7$

17) $77 \times$ _____ $= .77$

18) $652 \times$ _____ $= .652$

19) $646 \times$ _____ $= .646$

20) $642 \times$ _____ $= 6.42$

21) $35 \times$ _____ $= 3.5$

22) $26 \times$ _____ $= .26$

23) $834 \times$ _____ $= .834$

24) $849 \times$ _____ $= .849$

Multiplying by .1, .01 and .001

Multiply.

1) $412 \times .01 = $ _____

2) $145 \times .001 = $ _____

3) $775 \times .001 = $ _____

4) $85 \times .001 = $ _____

5) $844 \times .01 = $ _____

6) $24 \times .001 = $ _____

7) $43 \times .1 = $ _____

8) $421 \times .001 = $ _____

9) $81 \times .001 = $ _____

10) $463 \times .01 = $ _____

11) $537 \times .001 = $ _____

12) $62 \times .1 = $ _____

Fill in the blanks with .1, .01 or .001 to make the statements correct.

13) $404 \times $ _____ $= .404$

14) $21 \times $ _____ $= 2.1$

15) $869 \times $ _____ $= 86.9$

16) $16 \times $ _____ $= 1.6$

17) $122 \times $ _____ $= .122$

18) $56 \times $ _____ $= .56$

19) $697 \times $ _____ $= 69.7$

20) $88 \times $ _____ $= 8.8$

21) $96 \times $ _____ $= .096$

22) $619 \times $ _____ $= .619$

23) $702 \times $ _____ $= 70.2$

24) $766 \times $ _____ $= .766$

Multiplying by .1, .01 and .001

Multiply.

1) $862 \times .1 = $ _____

2) $749 \times .1 = $ _____

3) $740 \times .1 = $ _____

4) $55 \times .01 = $ _____

5) $773 \times .01 = $ _____

6) $463 \times .001 = $ _____

7) $570 \times .1 = $ _____

8) $27 \times .001 = $ _____

9) $37 \times .1 = $ _____

10) $22 \times .1 = $ _____

11) $424 \times .01 = $ _____

12) $24 \times .001 = $ _____

Fill in the blanks with .1, .01 or .001 to make the statements correct.

13) $833 \times $ _____ $= 8.33$

14) $860 \times $ _____ $= 86$

15) $643 \times $ _____ $= 64.3$

16) $611 \times $ _____ $= 6.11$

17) $58 \times $ _____ $= .58$

18) $168 \times $ _____ $= 16.8$

19) $96 \times $ _____ $= .096$

20) $922 \times $ _____ $= .922$

21) $84 \times $ _____ $= .84$

22) $742 \times $ _____ $= 74.2$

23) $250 \times $ _____ $= 25$

24) $61 \times $ _____ $= .061$

Multiplying by .1, .01 and .001

Multiply.

1) $70 \times .1 =$ _____

2) $833 \times .001 =$ _____

3) $20 \times .001 =$ _____

4) $132 \times .001 =$ _____

5) $22 \times .01 =$ _____

6) $914 \times .1 =$ _____

7) $46 \times .01 =$ _____

8) $678 \times .001 =$ _____

9) $491 \times .1 =$ _____

10) $640 \times .1 =$ _____

11) $59 \times .1 =$ _____

12) $75 \times .1 =$ _____

Fill in the blanks with .1, .01 or .001 to make the statements correct.

13) $29 \times$ _____ $= .029$

14) $23 \times$ _____ $= .023$

15) $98 \times$ _____ $= .98$

16) $48 \times$ _____ $= .48$

17) $15 \times$ _____ $= 1.5$

18) $344 \times$ _____ $= 3.44$

19) $17 \times$ _____ $= .17$

20) $42 \times$ _____ $= .042$

21) $699 \times$ _____ $= 69.9$

22) $295 \times$ _____ $= 29.5$

23) $435 \times$ _____ $= 43.5$

24) $76 \times$ _____ $= .76$

Multiplying by .1, .01 and .001

Multiply.

1) $64 \times .001 =$ _____

2) $882 \times .1 =$ _____

3) $24 \times .01 =$ _____

4) $624 \times .001 =$ _____

5) $93 \times .1 =$ _____

6) $21 \times .001 =$ _____

7) $143 \times .1 =$ _____

8) $30 \times .1 =$ _____

9) $661 \times .01 =$ _____

10) $885 \times .001 =$ _____

11) $927 \times .001 =$ _____

12) $826 \times .01 =$ _____

Fill in the blanks with .1, .01 or .001 to make the statements correct.

13) $98 \times$ _____ $= 9.8$

14) $816 \times$ _____ $= 8.16$

15) $19 \times$ _____ $= .19$

16) $723 \times$ _____ $= 7.23$

17) $85 \times$ _____ $= .085$

18) $44 \times$ _____ $= 4.4$

19) $17 \times$ _____ $= .017$

20) $29 \times$ _____ $= .29$

21) $157 \times$ _____ $= .157$

22) $712 \times$ _____ $= 71.2$

23) $25 \times$ _____ $= 2.5$

24) $883 \times$ _____ $= .883$

Multiplying by .1, .01 and .001

Multiply.

1) $187 \times .01 =$ _____

2) $11 \times .01 =$ _____

3) $45 \times .1 =$ _____

4) $63 \times .01 =$ _____

5) $522 \times .001 =$ _____

6) $769 \times .1 =$ _____

7) $31 \times .001 =$ _____

8) $742 \times .01 =$ _____

9) $96 \times .01 =$ _____

10) $444 \times .01 =$ _____

11) $359 \times .01 =$ _____

12) $250 \times .1 =$ _____

Fill in the blanks with .1, .01 or .001 to make the statements correct.

13) $85 \times$ _____ $= 8.5$

14) $150 \times$ _____ $= .15$

15) $515 \times$ _____ $= .515$

16) $487 \times$ _____ $= 4.87$

17) $550 \times$ _____ $= .55$

18) $262 \times$ _____ $= .262$

19) $922 \times$ _____ $= 92.2$

20) $50 \times$ _____ $= .5$

21) $24 \times$ _____ $= .024$

22) $465 \times$ _____ $= 4.65$

23) $63 \times$ _____ $= .063$

24) $753 \times$ _____ $= 7.53$

Multiplying by .1, .01 and .001

Multiply.

1) $55 \times .01 =$ _____

2) $743 \times .001 =$ _____

3) $21 \times .1 =$ _____

4) $14 \times .01 =$ _____

5) $277 \times .01 =$ _____

6) $259 \times .01 =$ _____

7) $44 \times .1 =$ _____

8) $29 \times .01 =$ _____

9) $987 \times .1 =$ _____

10) $49 \times .01 =$ _____

11) $32 \times .01 =$ _____

12) $81 \times .001 =$ _____

Fill in the blanks with .1, .01 or .001 to make the statements correct.

13) $755 \times$ _____ $= 7.55$

14) $217 \times$ _____ $= 2.17$

15) $50 \times$ _____ $= .05$

16) $54 \times$ _____ $= 5.4$

17) $69 \times$ _____ $= .069$

18) $780 \times$ _____ $= .78$

19) $27 \times$ _____ $= .027$

20) $812 \times$ _____ $= .812$

21) $36 \times$ _____ $= .36$

22) $249 \times$ _____ $= 2.49$

23) $364 \times$ _____ $= 36.4$

24) $277 \times$ _____ $= .277$

Multiplying by .1, .01 and .001

Multiply.

1) 77 x .01 = _____

2) 702 x .1 = _____

3) 88 x .001 = _____

4) 51 x .01 = _____

5) 94 x .1 = _____

6) 85 x .001 = _____

7) 744 x .01 = _____

8) 339 x .001 = _____

9) 776 x .001 = _____

10) 49 x .01 = _____

11) 32 x .01 = _____

12) 298 x .1 = _____

Fill in the blanks with .1, .01 or .001 to make the statements correct.

13) 28 x _____ = .28

14) 557 x _____ = 55.7

15) 209 x _____ = 2.09

16) 400 x _____ = 4

17) 63 x _____ = .063

18) 201 x _____ = 20.1

19) 22 x _____ = .022

20) 84 x _____ = .84

21) 37 x _____ = .037

22) 45 x _____ = 4.5

23) 591 x _____ = 59.1

24) 170 x _____ = .17

Multiplying by .1, .01 and .001

Multiply.

1) $260 \times .01 =$ _____

2) $325 \times .01 =$ _____

3) $406 \times .1 =$ _____

4) $973 \times .001 =$ _____

5) $687 \times .001 =$ _____

6) $64 \times .01 =$ _____

7) $540 \times .01 =$ _____

8) $657 \times .1 =$ _____

9) $44 \times .001 =$ _____

10) $31 \times .01 =$ _____

11) $49 \times .1 =$ _____

12) $55 \times .001 =$ _____

Fill in the blanks with .1, .01 or .001 to make the statements correct.

13) $863 \times$ _____ $= 8.63$

14) $869 \times$ _____ $= .869$

15) $855 \times$ _____ $= .855$

16) $14 \times$ _____ $= .014$

17) $165 \times$ _____ $= .165$

18) $840 \times$ _____ $= .84$

19) $23 \times$ _____ $= .23$

20) $25 \times$ _____ $= 2.5$

21) $734 \times$ _____ $= 73.4$

22) $421 \times$ _____ $= 4.21$

23) $303 \times$ _____ $= .303$

24) $51 \times$ _____ $= .51$

SECTION

MULTIPLYING DECIMALS BY 10, 100 & 1000

11 worksheets
24 problems per sheet

Name _____ Date _____

Multiplying Decimals by 10, 100 and 1000

Multiply.

1) .2 x 10 = _____

2) .038 x 10 = _____

3) .38 x 10 = _____

4) .049 x 1000 = _____

5) 2.1 x 100 = _____

6) .15 x 1000 = _____

7) .015 x 1000 = _____

8) 9.1 x 100 = _____

9) .67 x 10 = _____

10) 7.7 x 100 = _____

11) .73 x 100 = _____

12) .68 x 100 = _____

Fill in the blanks with 10, 100 or 1000 to make the statements correct.

13) .032 x _____ = 32

14) .63 x _____ = 63

15) .098 x _____ = 9.8

16) .099 x _____ = 9.9

17) 7.7 x _____ = 77

18) .2 x _____ = 20

19) .047 x _____ = 4.7

20) .057 x _____ = 57

21) .65 x _____ = 650

22) .48 x _____ = 4.8

23) .27 x _____ = 270

24) .4 x _____ = 40

Multiplying Decimals by 10, 100 and 1000

Multiply.

1) $3.7 \times 10 =$ _____

2) $7.4 \times 100 =$ _____

3) $.39 \times 100 =$ _____

4) $.89 \times 100 =$ _____

5) $.032 \times 10 =$ _____

6) $.62 \times 100 =$ _____

7) $.32 \times 100 =$ _____

8) $.076 \times 100 =$ _____

9) $.038 \times 1000 =$ _____

10) $.38 \times 100 =$ _____

11) $.095 \times 100 =$ _____

12) $.67 \times 10 =$ _____

Fill in the blanks with 10, 100 or 1000 to make the statements correct.

13) $.91 \times$ _____ $= 910$

14) $.012 \times$ _____ $= 12$

15) $.063 \times$ _____ $= .63$

16) $.59 \times$ _____ $= 590$

17) $.037 \times$ _____ $= 37$

18) $.97 \times$ _____ $= 970$

19) $9.1 \times$ _____ $= 91$

20) $.062 \times$ _____ $= .62$

21) $.032 \times$ _____ $= 32$

22) $.084 \times$ _____ $= 8.4$

23) $.6 \times$ _____ $= 6$

24) $.074 \times$ _____ $= .74$

www.claymaze.com

Multiplying Decimals by 10, 100 and 1000

Multiply.

1) $.095 \times 100 =$ _____

2) $.16 \times 100 =$ _____

3) $7.5 \times 100 =$ _____

4) $2.5 \times 10 =$ _____

5) $.049 \times 10 =$ _____

6) $.092 \times 1000 =$ _____

7) $.52 \times 10 =$ _____

8) $.19 \times 10 =$ _____

9) $.031 \times 10 =$ _____

10) $.13 \times 1000 =$ _____

11) $.15 \times 10 =$ _____

12) $.24 \times 1000 =$ _____

Fill in the blanks with 10, 100 or 1000 to make the statements correct.

13) $.054 \times$ _____ $= 5.4$

14) $.77 \times$ _____ $= 770$

15) $.88 \times$ _____ $= 880$

16) $.23 \times$ _____ $= 23$

17) $.53 \times$ _____ $= 530$

18) $.91 \times$ _____ $= 910$

19) $.71 \times$ _____ $= 7.1$

20) $.067 \times$ _____ $= .67$

21) $.51 \times$ _____ $= 5.1$

22) $.33 \times$ _____ $= 330$

23) $5.2 \times$ _____ $= 520$

24) $.078 \times$ _____ $= 78$

Multiplying Decimals by 10, 100 and 1000

Multiply.

1) .075 x 100 = _____

2) .027 x 1000 = _____

3) .48 x 1000 = _____

4) 2.1 x 10 = _____

5) .077 x 100 = _____

6) .26 x 100 = _____

7) .093 x 1000 = _____

8) .053 x 1000 = _____

9) .73 x 10 = _____

10) 9.4 x 10 = _____

11) .075 x 10 = _____

12) .33 x 100 = _____

Fill in the blanks with 10, 100 or 1000 to make the statements correct.

13) .52 x _____ = 52

14) .031 x _____ = 3.1

15) .62 x _____ = 62

16) 8.1 x _____ = 810

17) .081 x _____ = 8.1

18) .6 x _____ = 600

19) 3.7 x _____ = 37

20) .06 x _____ = 6

21) .2 x _____ = 2

22) .12 x _____ = 1.2

23) .091 x _____ = 9.1

24) .62 x _____ = 6.2

Multiplying Decimals by 10, 100 and 1000

Multiply.

1) $.091 \times 100 =$ _____

2) $.31 \times 10 =$ _____

3) $.2 \times 10 =$ _____

4) $9.5 \times 100 =$ _____

5) $.099 \times 10 =$ _____

6) $.79 \times 100 =$ _____

7) $.48 \times 100 =$ _____

8) $.083 \times 100 =$ _____

9) $.014 \times 10 =$ _____

10) $.61 \times 1000 =$ _____

11) $.43 \times 10 =$ _____

12) $1.6 \times 100 =$ _____

Fill in the blanks with 10, 100 or 1000 to make the statements correct.

13) $.077 \times$ _____ $= 77$

14) $4.2 \times$ _____ $= 42$

15) $.012 \times$ _____ $= 12$

16) $7.4 \times$ _____ $= 740$

17) $.76 \times$ _____ $= 760$

18) $.031 \times$ _____ $= 3.1$

19) $.06 \times$ _____ $= 60$

20) $.016 \times$ _____ $= 16$

21) $.72 \times$ _____ $= 72$

22) $.061 \times$ _____ $= 6.1$

23) $.92 \times$ _____ $= 92$

24) $.64 \times$ _____ $= 6.4$

Multiplying Decimals by 10, 100 and 1000

Multiply.

1) .047 x 100 = _____

2) .084 x 1000 = _____

3) .08 x 10 = _____

4) .81 x 100 = _____

5) .033 x 1000 = _____

6) .45 x 10 = _____

7) .062 x 10 = _____

8) 2.1 x 10 = _____

9) .27 x 10 = _____

10) .041 x 1000 = _____

11) .48 x 10 = _____

12) .49 x 1000 = _____

Fill in the blanks with 10, 100 or 1000 to make the statements correct.

13) .03 x _____ = .3

14) .015 x _____ = .15

15) .88 x _____ = 880

16) 6.4 x _____ = 640

17) .91 x _____ = 910

18) .3 x _____ = 30

19) .075 x _____ = 7.5

20) .26 x _____ = 2.6

21) 5.4 x _____ = 54

22) .028 x _____ = 28

23) .59 x _____ = 59

24) .74 x _____ = 740

Multiplying Decimals by 10, 100 and 1000

Multiply.

1) $.061 \times 1000 =$ _____

2) $.023 \times 100 =$ _____

3) $.11 \times 1000 =$ _____

4) $.32 \times 100 =$ _____

5) $.81 \times 1000 =$ _____

6) $8.5 \times 10 =$ _____

7) $.048 \times 10 =$ _____

8) $.31 \times 10 =$ _____

9) $8.9 \times 10 =$ _____

10) $.38 \times 100 =$ _____

11) $9.4 \times 100 =$ _____

12) $.056 \times 1000 =$ _____

Fill in the blanks with 10, 100 or 1000 to make the statements correct.

13) $.46 \times$ _____ $= 46$

14) $.08 \times$ _____ $= .8$

15) $6.2 \times$ _____ $= 620$

16) $9.5 \times$ _____ $= 95$

17) $.42 \times$ _____ $= 420$

18) $5.4 \times$ _____ $= 54$

19) $.031 \times$ _____ $= 3.1$

20) $.5 \times$ _____ $= 500$

21) $.055 \times$ _____ $= 55$

22) $2.1 \times$ _____ $= 210$

23) $.047 \times$ _____ $= .47$

24) $.62 \times$ _____ $= 6.2$

Multiplying Decimals by 10, 100 and 1000

Multiply.

1) $2.6 \times 10 =$ _____

2) $.15 \times 10 =$ _____

3) $.26 \times 10 =$ _____

4) $.032 \times 1000 =$ _____

5) $4.2 \times 100 =$ _____

6) $.61 \times 100 =$ _____

7) $1.8 \times 100 =$ _____

8) $.74 \times 100 =$ _____

9) $.079 \times 10 =$ _____

10) $.097 \times 100 =$ _____

11) $.21 \times 10 =$ _____

12) $.51 \times 1000 =$ _____

Fill in the blanks with 10, 100 or 1000 to make the statements correct.

13) $.094 \times$ _____ $= 9.4$

14) $.61 \times$ _____ $= 610$

15) $5.7 \times$ _____ $= 57$

16) $.055 \times$ _____ $= 55$

17) $.85 \times$ _____ $= 85$

18) $.64 \times$ _____ $= 6.4$

19) $7.7 \times$ _____ $= 770$

20) $.019 \times$ _____ $= 19$

21) $.86 \times$ _____ $= 8.6$

22) $.54 \times$ _____ $= 54$

23) $.085 \times$ _____ $= 8.5$

24) $.027 \times$ _____ $= 27$

Name _____   Date _____

Multiplying Decimals by 10, 100 and 1000

Multiply.

1) .16 x 10 = _____

2) .44 x 1000 = _____

3) .5 x 1000 = _____

4) .05 x 10 = _____

5) 1.6 x 10 = _____

6) .091 x 1000 = _____

7) .092 x 1000 = _____

8) .6 x 1000 = _____

9) .08 x 100 = _____

10) 4.2 x 10 = _____

11) .015 x 1000 = _____

12) .025 x 100 = _____

Fill in the blanks with 10, 100 or 1000 to make the statements correct.

13) .96 x _____ = 96

14) .082 x _____ = 82

15) .31 x _____ = 3.1

16) .36 x _____ = 360

17) .9 x _____ = 90

18) .037 x _____ = 37

19) 7.5 x _____ = 750

20) .88 x _____ = 8.8

21) .92 x _____ = 92

22) .047 x _____ = .47

23) .098 x _____ = .98

24) 4.2 x _____ = 420

www.claymaze.com

Multiplying Decimals by 10, 100 and 1000

Multiply.

1) .096 x 1000 = _____

2) .024 x 10 = _____

3) .31 x 100 = _____

4) .097 x 1000 = _____

5) 3.7 x 10 = _____

6) .89 x 100 = _____

7) .011 x 1000 = _____

8) .05 x 10 = _____

9) .062 x 10 = _____

10) 4.1 x 100 = _____

11) .36 x 100 = _____

12) .055 x 100 = _____

Fill in the blanks with 10, 100 or 1000 to make the statements correct.

13) .74 x _____ = 7.4

14) .056 x _____ = .56

15) .84 x _____ = 840

16) .044 x _____ = 44

17) .77 x _____ = 770

18) .48 x _____ = 48

19) .76 x _____ = 76

20) 8.6 x _____ = 860

21) .038 x _____ = .38

22) .53 x _____ = 530

23) .058 x _____ = 58

24) .93 x _____ = 9.3

Name _____   Date _____

Multiplying Decimals by 10, 100 and 1000

Multiply.

1) .056 x 10 = _____   2) 4.2 x 100 = _____

3) .45 x 100 = _____   4) .76 x 100 = _____

5) .34 x 100 = _____   6) .2 x 1000 = _____

7) .39 x 100 = _____   8) 6.2 x 10 = _____

9) .016 x 1000 = _____   10) .08 x 10 = _____

11) 8.4 x 10 = _____   12) .064 x 10 = _____

Fill in the blanks with 10, 100 or 1000 to make the statements correct.

13) .019 x _____ = 19   14) 7.5 x _____ = 750

15) 2.1 x _____ = 210   16) .022 x _____ = 22

17) .055 x _____ = 55   18) .02 x _____ = .2

19) .27 x _____ = 27   20) .74 x _____ = 7.4

21) .03 x _____ = 30   22) .025 x _____ = 2.5

23) .037 x _____ = 37   24) .22 x _____ = 2.2

www.claymaze.com

SECTION

DECIMAL ADDITION AND SUBTRACTION

11 worksheets
18 problems per sheet

Decimal Addition and Subtraction

Add.

1) $\begin{array}{r} 63.15 \\ +4.2 \\ \hline \end{array}$
2) $\begin{array}{r} 14 \\ +45.28 \\ \hline \end{array}$
3) $\begin{array}{r} 6.79 \\ +61.1 \\ \hline \end{array}$
4) $\begin{array}{r} 9.4 \\ +53.18 \\ \hline \end{array}$

5) $\begin{array}{r} 6.2 \\ +21.34 \\ \hline \end{array}$
6) $\begin{array}{r} 59.55 \\ +.16 \\ \hline \end{array}$
7) $\begin{array}{r} 3.36 \\ +27.2 \\ \hline \end{array}$
8) $\begin{array}{r} 46.11 \\ +.26 \\ \hline \end{array}$

Subtract.

9) $\begin{array}{r} 33 \\ -4.7 \\ \hline \end{array}$
10) $\begin{array}{r} 94.02 \\ -86.14 \\ \hline \end{array}$
11) $\begin{array}{r} 39.49 \\ -6.7 \\ \hline \end{array}$
12) $\begin{array}{r} 83.41 \\ -82.7 \\ \hline \end{array}$

13) $\begin{array}{r} 72.31 \\ -.11 \\ \hline \end{array}$
14) $\begin{array}{r} 43.13 \\ -2.4 \\ \hline \end{array}$
15) $\begin{array}{r} 28.34 \\ -5.7 \\ \hline \end{array}$
16) $\begin{array}{r} 65.08 \\ -57.18 \\ \hline \end{array}$

Add and Subtract. *(Remember to line up the decimal points.)*

17) $46 + 39.67$

18) $30.2 - 26.41$

Decimal Addition and Subtraction

Add.

1) $\begin{array}{r} 17.37 \\ +1.5 \\ \hline \end{array}$
2) $\begin{array}{r} 27.7 \\ +42.77 \\ \hline \end{array}$
3) $\begin{array}{r} 8.82 \\ +73.86 \\ \hline \end{array}$
4) $\begin{array}{r} 6.22 \\ +75.5 \\ \hline \end{array}$

5) $\begin{array}{r} 3.7 \\ +62.26 \\ \hline \end{array}$
6) $\begin{array}{r} 23.8 \\ +14.44 \\ \hline \end{array}$
7) $\begin{array}{r} 18.8 \\ +33.56 \\ \hline \end{array}$
8) $\begin{array}{r} 16 \\ +59.69 \\ \hline \end{array}$

Subtract.

9) $\begin{array}{r} 18.55 \\ -2.4 \\ \hline \end{array}$
10) $\begin{array}{r} 48.57 \\ -44.07 \\ \hline \end{array}$
11) $\begin{array}{r} 61 \\ -34.68 \\ \hline \end{array}$
12) $\begin{array}{r} 84.63 \\ -1.2 \\ \hline \end{array}$

13) $\begin{array}{r} 73.19 \\ -.24 \\ \hline \end{array}$
14) $\begin{array}{r} 59.75 \\ -24.75 \\ \hline \end{array}$
15) $\begin{array}{r} 20.26 \\ -1.6 \\ \hline \end{array}$
16) $\begin{array}{r} 42 \\ -4.31 \\ \hline \end{array}$

Add and Subtract. *(Remember to line up the decimal points.)*

17) $.76 + 59.4$

18) $60.95 - 2.5$

Decimal Addition and Subtraction

Add.

1)   45.8
  +50.26

2)   1.35
  +65.5

3)   .73
  +75.8

4)   8.9
  +59.27

5)   13.6
  +24.62

6)   .91
  +36.5

7)   24.53
  + 3.65

8)   3.2
  +74.83

Subtract.

9)   24.15
  -17.75

10)   77.6
  - 1.88

11)   43.24
  - 8.6

12)   85.72
  -49.75

13)   48
  - 4.98

14)   21.07
  -20.3

15)   63.93
  -59.23

16)   60.43
  - .46

Add and Subtract. *(Remember to line up the decimal points.)*

17) 59.35 + 26

18) 62 − 8.18

Decimal Addition and Subtraction

Add.

1)   9.64
   +28.1
   _____

2) 13.3
   +17.37
   _____

3) 44.6
   +46.68
   _____

4)   .27
   +24.21
   _____

5) 38.65
   +   .64
   _____

6)   9.4
   +42.83
   _____

7) 23.03
   + 4.97
   _____

8)   9.5
   +59.59
   _____

Subtract.

9)   44.1
   - 3.89
   _____

10) 46.86
   - 5.9
   _____

11) 31.29
   -23.27
   _____

12) 98
   -73.58
   _____

13) 30.09
   -27.59
   _____

14) 29
   - 3.52
   _____

15) 16.02
   - 1.4
   _____

16) 49.96
   -44.46
   _____

Add and Subtract. *(Remember to line up the decimal points.)*

17) 7.03 + 83.2

18) 15.82 - .23

Decimal Addition and Subtraction

Add.

1) 32.53
  + .74

2)   5.4
  +59.72

3) 46.2
  +27.34

4)   1.52
  +16.8

5)   5.2
  +62.59

6)   2.5
  +32.53

7) 43
  +11.08

8)   8.9
  +32.74

Subtract.

9) 46.07
  - 5.2

10) 24.8
  - .59

11) 68
  -45.82

12) 54.73
  -53.16

13) 57.32
  - .9

14) 74
  -28.06

15) 72.83
  -29.93

16) 81.17
  - 7.5

Add and Subtract. *(Remember to line up the decimal points.)*

17) 14 + 47.41

18) 30.4 - 5.95

Decimal Addition and Subtraction

Add.

1) 8.6
   +87.42
   _____

2) 17.62
   + 5.7
   _____

3) 73.88
   + 5.65
   _____

4) 52.86
   + .17
   _____

5) 6.95
   +11.5
   _____

6) 1.8
   +60.56
   _____

7)   .87
   +33.6
   _____

8) 7.67
   +91.1
   _____

Subtract.

9) 47.92
   -46.32
   _____

10) 55
   -47.61
   _____

11) 70.69
   - 6.9
   _____

12) 40.03
   -35.53
   _____

13) 58.2
   -57.67
   _____

14) 23.1
   - 4.01
   _____

15) 70
   -62.35
   _____

16) 68.2
   - 6.04
   _____

Add and Subtract. *(Remember to line up the decimal points.)*

17) 7.33 + 14

18) 47.75 - .98

Decimal Addition and Subtraction

Add.

1) 28.53
   +59.1
   _____

2) 29.24
   + 3.62
   _____

3) 62.1
   +15.75
   _____

4) 15.4
   +34.39
   _____

5) 21.7
   +69.58
   _____

6)   2.1
   +17.93
   _____

7)   8.41
   +85.5
   _____

8) 30.01
   + 8.18
   _____

Subtract.

9)   68
   - 3.67
   _____

10) 23.11
   -20.61
   _____

11) 58.91
   - 4.4
   _____

12) 51.62
   -   .83
   _____

13) 96.19
   - 6.7
   _____

14) 71.21
   - 8.1
   _____

15) 84
   -59.25
   _____

16) 35.39
   -28.53
   _____

Add and Subtract. *(Remember to line up the decimal points.)*

17) 12 + 46.41

18) 26.24 - 5.01

Decimal Addition and Subtraction

Add.

1)   52.6
  +28.29

2) 15.16
  + 6.5

3)   9.1
  +50.04

4) 86
  +13.72

5)   3.1
  +58.47

6) 35.6
  +14.15

7)   5.5
  +41.74

8) 6.29
  +13.15

Subtract.

9) 58
  -10.09

10) 36.75
  - 6.5

11) 82.8
  -28.58

12) 37
  -11.74

13) 97.72
  -52.72

14) 89.1
  -48.03

15) 75.57
  - 5.5

16) 20.61
  -15.41

Add and Subtract. *(Remember to line up the decimal points.)*

17) .77 + 68

18) 81.2 - 27.65

Decimal Addition and Subtraction

Add.

1) 2.54
   +38.1
   ‾‾‾‾‾

2) 13
   +46.42
   ‾‾‾‾‾

3) 41.04
   + 7.7
   ‾‾‾‾‾

4)   .24
   +93.2
   ‾‾‾‾‾

5) 67.55
   + 7.15
   ‾‾‾‾‾

6) 50.36
   + .31
   ‾‾‾‾‾

7) 19.2
   +77.56
   ‾‾‾‾‾

8)   .79
   +36.93
   ‾‾‾‾‾

Subtract.

9) 42.07
   -34.17
   ‾‾‾‾‾

10) 27.1
   -26.55
   ‾‾‾‾‾

11) 64
   - .49
   ‾‾‾‾‾

12) 23.46
   -18.25
   ‾‾‾‾‾

13) 57.47
   -15.1
   ‾‾‾‾‾

14) 74.52
   -60.57
   ‾‾‾‾‾

15) 75.2
   -38.97
   ‾‾‾‾‾

16) 97
   -64.49
   ‾‾‾‾‾

Add and Subtract. *(Remember to line up the decimal points.)*

17) 3.32 + 15.74

18) 98.3 - 38.35

Decimal Addition and Subtraction

Add.

1)
```
  17.79
+  4.78
-------
```

2)
```
   1.3
+29.89
-------
```

3)
```
  43.8
+11.73
-------
```

4)
```
  26.27
+  1.5
-------
```

5)
```
  54.78
+  3.85
-------
```

6)
```
    .85
+38.58
-------
```

7)
```
   2.1
+86.09
-------
```

8)
```
   5.93
+30.42
-------
```

Subtract.

9)
```
  79
-45.21
-------
```

10)
```
  84.54
-   .92
-------
```

11)
```
  81.5
-57.36
-------
```

12)
```
  51.17
-22.19
-------
```

13)
```
  90.27
-  7.62
-------
```

14)
```
  28.9
-  3.76
-------
```

15)
```
  49.21
-47.68
-------
```

16)
```
  65.4
-22.75
-------
```

Add and Subtract. *(Remember to line up the decimal points.)*

17) 4.74 + 21.23

18) 42 − 28.53

Decimal Addition and Subtraction

Add.

1)   60.65
   + .38
      ‾‾‾‾‾‾

2)   1.5
   +48.93
      ‾‾‾‾‾‾

3)   14
   +79.52
      ‾‾‾‾‾‾

4)   59.8
   +22.94
      ‾‾‾‾‾‾

5)   6.5
   +49.41
      ‾‾‾‾‾‾

6)   15.25
   + .73
      ‾‾‾‾‾‾

7)   6.4
   +28.52
      ‾‾‾‾‾‾

8)   8.27
   +19.7
      ‾‾‾‾‾‾

Subtract.

9)   81.46
   -27.23
      ‾‾‾‾‾‾

10)   20
   -19.89
      ‾‾‾‾‾‾

11)   62.83
   - 3.48
      ‾‾‾‾‾‾

12)   74.05
   - .08
      ‾‾‾‾‾‾

13)   16
   -12.22
      ‾‾‾‾‾‾

14)   20.14
   -19.28
      ‾‾‾‾‾‾

15)   34.1
   - 2.03
      ‾‾‾‾‾‾

16)   18.24
   -14.54
      ‾‾‾‾‾‾

Add and Subtract. *(Remember to line up the decimal points.)*

17) 3.2 + 21.69

18) 76.8 - 32.78

SECTION

DECIMAL MULTIPLICATION 1-DIGIT AND 2-DIGIT NUMBERS

11 worksheets
27 problems per sheet

Decimal Multiplication 1-Digit and 2-Digit Numbers

Multiply.

1) .4 x .3 = _____   2) .7 x 9 = _____   3) 5 x .4 = _____

4) .5 x .5 = _____   5) .6 x .6 = _____   6) .7 x 2 = _____

7) .4 x .6 = _____   8) 4 x .2 = _____   9) .6 x .7 = _____

10) 8 x .5 = _____   11) 9 x .4 = _____   12) .9 x 3 = _____

13) .5 x .2 = _____   14) .2 x 4 = _____   15) .3 x .6 = _____

Multiply.

16)   3.7
    x 8
    _____

17)   98
    x.2
    _____

18)   7.5
    x 4
    _____

19)   49
    x.5
    _____

20)   3.6
    x.9
    _____

21)   2.7
    x 4
    _____

22)   5.7
    x 5
    _____

23)   2.5
    x.9
    _____

24)   2.6
    x 4
    _____

25)   39
    x.9
    _____

26)   37
    x.5
    _____

27)   25
    x.4
    _____

Decimal Multiplication | 1-Digit and 2-Digit Numbers

Multiply.

1) $2 \times .3 =$ _____   2) $.7 \times .9 =$ _____   3) $.8 \times .5 =$ _____

4) $.5 \times 7 =$ _____   5) $.2 \times 8 =$ _____   6) $8 \times .9 =$ _____

7) $5 \times .4 =$ _____   8) $.5 \times .6 =$ _____   9) $6 \times .5 =$ _____

10) $.3 \times 4 =$ _____   11) $9 \times .8 =$ _____   12) $.3 \times .3 =$ _____

13) $.6 \times .7 =$ _____   14) $.4 \times 4 =$ _____   15) $.5 \times .9 =$ _____

Multiply.

16) $\begin{array}{r} 2.7 \\ \times\,.8 \\ \hline \end{array}$ 17) $\begin{array}{r} 20 \\ \times\,.5 \\ \hline \end{array}$ 18) $\begin{array}{r} 7.4 \\ \times\,7 \\ \hline \end{array}$ 19) $\begin{array}{r} 81 \\ \times\,.9 \\ \hline \end{array}$

20) $\begin{array}{r} 54 \\ \times\,.4 \\ \hline \end{array}$ 21) $\begin{array}{r} 98 \\ \times\,.2 \\ \hline \end{array}$ 22) $\begin{array}{r} 33 \\ \times\,.5 \\ \hline \end{array}$ 23) $\begin{array}{r} 57 \\ \times\,.8 \\ \hline \end{array}$

24) $\begin{array}{r} 28 \\ \times\,.9 \\ \hline \end{array}$ 25) $\begin{array}{r} 55 \\ \times\,.3 \\ \hline \end{array}$ 26) $\begin{array}{r} 2.2 \\ \times\,9 \\ \hline \end{array}$ 27) $\begin{array}{r} 1.5 \\ \times\,.5 \\ \hline \end{array}$

Decimal Multiplication   1-Digit and 2-Digit Numbers

Multiply.

1) $.9 \times .6 =$ _____
2) $.6 \times .2 =$ _____
3) $.3 \times .8 =$ _____

4) $.4 \times .3 =$ _____
5) $.7 \times .9 =$ _____
6) $2 \times .6 =$ _____

7) $.7 \times 9 =$ _____
8) $.5 \times .6 =$ _____
9) $5 \times .4 =$ _____

10) $.3 \times .6 =$ _____
11) $.7 \times .3 =$ _____
12) $.2 \times .5 =$ _____

13) $5 \times .7 =$ _____
14) $.4 \times .5 =$ _____
15) $.8 \times .6 =$ _____

Multiply.

16)
$$\begin{array}{r} 6.7 \\ \times\,.4 \\ \hline \end{array}$$

17)
$$\begin{array}{r} 5.7 \\ \times\,7 \\ \hline \end{array}$$

18)
$$\begin{array}{r} 62 \\ \times\,.4 \\ \hline \end{array}$$

19)
$$\begin{array}{r} 9.8 \\ \times\,2 \\ \hline \end{array}$$

20)
$$\begin{array}{r} 2.6 \\ \times\,4 \\ \hline \end{array}$$

21)
$$\begin{array}{r} 58 \\ \times\,.5 \\ \hline \end{array}$$

22)
$$\begin{array}{r} 90 \\ \times\,.9 \\ \hline \end{array}$$

23)
$$\begin{array}{r} 42 \\ \times\,.5 \\ \hline \end{array}$$

24)
$$\begin{array}{r} 17 \\ \times\,.9 \\ \hline \end{array}$$

25)
$$\begin{array}{r} 5.9 \\ \times\,5 \\ \hline \end{array}$$

26)
$$\begin{array}{r} 2.5 \\ \times\,4 \\ \hline \end{array}$$

27)
$$\begin{array}{r} 52 \\ \times\,.2 \\ \hline \end{array}$$

Decimal Multiplication   1-Digit and 2-Digit Numbers

Multiply.

1) .4 x 8 = _____   2) .5 x .9 = _____   3) .9 x 4 = _____

4) .2 x .5 = _____   5) .7 x .6 = _____   6) .6 x .3 = _____

7) .9 x .6 = _____   8) .6 x .5 = _____   9) .2 x .6 = _____

10) .3 x .7 = _____   11) 2 x .4 = _____   12) .5 x .3 = _____

13) 6 x .9 = _____   14) .6 x .7 = _____   15) .9 x .9 = _____

Multiply.

16)   5.7
    x 8
    _____

17)   98
    x .5
    _____

18)   8.4
    x 4
    _____

19)   90
    x .4
    _____

20)   29
    x .5
    _____

21)   4.3
    x .2
    _____

22)   12
    x .9
    _____

23)   64
    x .2
    _____

24)   21
    x .8
    _____

25)   4.7
    x .9
    _____

26)   4.3
    x .5
    _____

27)   89
    x .4
    _____

Decimal Multiplication 1-Digit and 2-Digit Numbers

Multiply.

1) $.7 \times .5 =$ _____

2) $.3 \times .4 =$ _____

3) $.2 \times .3 =$ _____

4) $.9 \times .9 =$ _____

5) $.6 \times .5 =$ _____

6) $.3 \times .9 =$ _____

7) $.6 \times .4 =$ _____

8) $8 \times .3 =$ _____

9) $.9 \times 7 =$ _____

10) $.3 \times .3 =$ _____

11) $.9 \times 9 =$ _____

12) $.4 \times .3 =$ _____

13) $.6 \times 8 =$ _____

14) $.8 \times .3 =$ _____

15) $5 \times .6 =$ _____

Multiply.

16)
$$\begin{array}{r} 1.8 \\ \times\ 2 \\ \hline \end{array}$$

17)
$$\begin{array}{r} 75 \\ \times .4 \\ \hline \end{array}$$

18)
$$\begin{array}{r} 44 \\ \times .2 \\ \hline \end{array}$$

19)
$$\begin{array}{r} 1.8 \\ \times\ 7 \\ \hline \end{array}$$

20)
$$\begin{array}{r} 2.2 \\ \times\ 5 \\ \hline \end{array}$$

21)
$$\begin{array}{r} 2.1 \\ \times\ 8 \\ \hline \end{array}$$

22)
$$\begin{array}{r} 87 \\ \times .5 \\ \hline \end{array}$$

23)
$$\begin{array}{r} 5.2 \\ \times .2 \\ \hline \end{array}$$

24)
$$\begin{array}{r} 47 \\ \times .4 \\ \hline \end{array}$$

25)
$$\begin{array}{r} 70 \\ \times .5 \\ \hline \end{array}$$

26)
$$\begin{array}{r} 23 \\ \times .9 \\ \hline \end{array}$$

27)
$$\begin{array}{r} 4.7 \\ \times\ 5 \\ \hline \end{array}$$

www.claymaze.com

Decimal Multiplication   1-Digit and 2-Digit Numbers

Multiply.

1) $.5 \times .7 =$ _____   2) $.6 \times .5 =$ _____   3) $.3 \times .9 =$ _____

4) $.9 \times 4 =$ _____   5) $.7 \times .9 =$ _____   6) $.5 \times 4 =$ _____

7) $.6 \times .2 =$ _____   8) $4 \times .8 =$ _____   9) $.6 \times .9 =$ _____

10) $8 \times .7 =$ _____   11) $.6 \times .6 =$ _____   12) $.5 \times .4 =$ _____

13) $.3 \times .8 =$ _____   14) $.2 \times 5 =$ _____   15) $.3 \times .6 =$ _____

Multiply.

16) $\begin{array}{r} 1.6 \\ \times\ 2 \\ \hline \end{array}$ 17) $\begin{array}{r} 13 \\ \times.4 \\ \hline \end{array}$ 18) $\begin{array}{r} 36 \\ \times.8 \\ \hline \end{array}$ 19) $\begin{array}{r} 3.7 \\ \times.9 \\ \hline \end{array}$

20) $\begin{array}{r} 7.7 \\ \times\ 5 \\ \hline \end{array}$ 21) $\begin{array}{r} 91 \\ \times.8 \\ \hline \end{array}$ 22) $\begin{array}{r} 20 \\ \times.4 \\ \hline \end{array}$ 23) $\begin{array}{r} 2.7 \\ \times\ 5 \\ \hline \end{array}$

24) $\begin{array}{r} 54 \\ \times.4 \\ \hline \end{array}$ 25) $\begin{array}{r} 59 \\ \times.5 \\ \hline \end{array}$ 26) $\begin{array}{r} 33 \\ \times.9 \\ \hline \end{array}$ 27) $\begin{array}{r} 54 \\ \times.2 \\ \hline \end{array}$

Decimal Multiplication | 1-Digit and 2-Digit Numbers

Multiply.

1) $4 \times .4 =$ _____ 2) $.2 \times .6 =$ _____ 3) $.6 \times .7 =$ _____

4) $8 \times .8 =$ _____ 5) $.9 \times .7 =$ _____ 6) $.4 \times .3 =$ _____

7) $.5 \times 6 =$ _____ 8) $.7 \times .3 =$ _____ 9) $.8 \times .6 =$ _____

10) $5 \times .3 =$ _____ 11) $.4 \times 4 =$ _____ 12) $.3 \times .3 =$ _____

13) $.9 \times .6 =$ _____ 14) $9 \times .2 =$ _____ 15) $.8 \times 5 =$ _____

Multiply.

16)
$$\begin{array}{r} 5.2 \\ \times .2 \\ \hline \end{array}$$

17)
$$\begin{array}{r} 93 \\ \times .9 \\ \hline \end{array}$$

18)
$$\begin{array}{r} 3.5 \\ \times .5 \\ \hline \end{array}$$

19)
$$\begin{array}{r} 6.2 \\ \times 2 \\ \hline \end{array}$$

20)
$$\begin{array}{r} 5.5 \\ \times .5 \\ \hline \end{array}$$

21)
$$\begin{array}{r} 89 \\ \times .8 \\ \hline \end{array}$$

22)
$$\begin{array}{r} 98 \\ \times .9 \\ \hline \end{array}$$

23)
$$\begin{array}{r} 6.7 \\ \times 7 \\ \hline \end{array}$$

24)
$$\begin{array}{r} 62 \\ \times .8 \\ \hline \end{array}$$

25)
$$\begin{array}{r} 36 \\ \times .9 \\ \hline \end{array}$$

26)
$$\begin{array}{r} 6.5 \\ \times 4 \\ \hline \end{array}$$

27)
$$\begin{array}{r} 44 \\ \times .5 \\ \hline \end{array}$$

Decimal Multiplication   1-Digit and 2-Digit Numbers

Multiply.

1) $4 \times .2 = $ _____

2) $.3 \times .5 = $ _____

3) $.6 \times .4 = $ _____

4) $.8 \times .5 = $ _____

5) $.7 \times 8 = $ _____

6) $.5 \times .6 = $ _____

7) $.6 \times .8 = $ _____

8) $.9 \times .6 = $ _____

9) $9 \times .2 = $ _____

10) $.3 \times .9 = $ _____

11) $.5 \times .5 = $ _____

12) $.2 \times 5 = $ _____

13) $.5 \times 6 = $ _____

14) $.3 \times .2 = $ _____

15) $.7 \times .5 = $ _____

Multiply.

16) $\begin{array}{r} 7.4 \\ \times .8 \\ \hline \end{array}$

17) $\begin{array}{r} 68 \\ \times .9 \\ \hline \end{array}$

18) $\begin{array}{r} 88 \\ \times .5 \\ \hline \end{array}$

19) $\begin{array}{r} 83 \\ \times .2 \\ \hline \end{array}$

20) $\begin{array}{r} 45 \\ \times .9 \\ \hline \end{array}$

21) $\begin{array}{r} 31 \\ \times .5 \\ \hline \end{array}$

22) $\begin{array}{r} 75 \\ \times .2 \\ \hline \end{array}$

23) $\begin{array}{r} 94 \\ \times .5 \\ \hline \end{array}$

24) $\begin{array}{r} 13 \\ \times .4 \\ \hline \end{array}$

25) $\begin{array}{r} 1.8 \\ \times 8 \\ \hline \end{array}$

26) $\begin{array}{r} 5.2 \\ \times .8 \\ \hline \end{array}$

27) $\begin{array}{r} 73 \\ \times .9 \\ \hline \end{array}$

www.claymaze.com

Decimal Multiplication   1-Digit and 2-Digit Numbers

Multiply.

1) .6 x .3 = _____   2) 9 x .2 = _____   3) .6 x .7 = _____

4) 2 x .5 = _____   5) .2 x 4 = _____   6) .3 x .4 = _____

7) .9 x 3 = _____   8) .7 x .3 = _____   9) .5 x .7 = _____

10) 9 x .9 = _____   11) .6 x .8 = _____   12) 6 x .9 = _____

13) .9 x .3 = _____   14) .4 x 8 = _____   15) .8 x .5 = _____

Multiply.

16)
```
   5.7
 x   4
_____
```

17)
```
   22
 x .9
_____
```

18)
```
   57
 x .5
_____
```

19)
```
   65
 x .4
_____
```

20)
```
   45
 x .3
_____
```

21)
```
   9.5
 x   6
_____
```

22)
```
   80
 x .2
_____
```

23)
```
   3.4
 x .7
_____
```

24)
```
   27
 x .4
_____
```

25)
```
   79
 x .2
_____
```

26)
```
   7.7
 x .5
_____
```

27)
```
   32
 x .8
_____
```

Decimal Multiplication   1-Digit and 2-Digit Numbers

Multiply.

1) .6 x .4 = _____   2) 2 x .7 = _____   3) .6 x 7 = _____

4) .5 x 9 = _____   5) .4 x .5 = _____   6) .7 x 2 = _____

7) 3 x .9 = _____   8) .3 x .4 = _____   9) .6 x .7 = _____

10) .3 x .2 = _____   11) 5 x .8 = _____   12) .8 x .3 = _____

13) .6 x .8 = _____   14) .9 x 4 = _____   15) .7 x .5 = _____

Multiply.

16)   1.8
  x 2
_____

17)   1.3
  x .4
_____

18)   6.5
  x 6
_____

19)   60
  x .8
_____

20)   64
  x .8
_____

21)   9.4
  x 7
_____

22)   1.8
  x .9
_____

23)   97
  x .5
_____

24)   30
  x .9
_____

25)   13
  x .5
_____

26)   57
  x .4
_____

27)   32
  x .9
_____

www.claymaze.com

Decimal Multiplication | 1-Digit and 2-Digit Numbers

Multiply.

1) $2 \times .2 =$ _____

2) $.2 \times .6 =$ _____

3) $5 \times .7 =$ _____

4) $.7 \times .6 =$ _____

5) $7 \times .3 =$ _____

6) $.3 \times .6 =$ _____

7) $.9 \times 6 =$ _____

8) $8 \times .2 =$ _____

9) $.5 \times .5 =$ _____

10) $.8 \times 5 =$ _____

11) $.3 \times .5 =$ _____

12) $9 \times .7 =$ _____

13) $.3 \times 2 =$ _____

14) $9 \times .4 =$ _____

15) $4 \times .5 =$ _____

Multiply.

16)
$$\begin{array}{r} 1.3 \\ \times\, .8 \\ \hline \end{array}$$

17)
$$\begin{array}{r} 5.4 \\ \times\, 4 \\ \hline \end{array}$$

18)
$$\begin{array}{r} 40 \\ \times\, .8 \\ \hline \end{array}$$

19)
$$\begin{array}{r} 3.5 \\ \times\, 3 \\ \hline \end{array}$$

20)
$$\begin{array}{r} 6.7 \\ \times\, .4 \\ \hline \end{array}$$

21)
$$\begin{array}{r} 1.1 \\ \times\, 2 \\ \hline \end{array}$$

22)
$$\begin{array}{r} 2.6 \\ \times\, 5 \\ \hline \end{array}$$

23)
$$\begin{array}{r} 21 \\ \times\, .7 \\ \hline \end{array}$$

24)
$$\begin{array}{r} 4.4 \\ \times\, 8 \\ \hline \end{array}$$

25)
$$\begin{array}{r} 2.2 \\ \times\, 9 \\ \hline \end{array}$$

26)
$$\begin{array}{r} 6.7 \\ \times\, .4 \\ \hline \end{array}$$

27)
$$\begin{array}{r} 5.5 \\ \times\, .7 \\ \hline \end{array}$$

    www.claymaze.com

SECTION

DECIMAL MULTIPLICATION 3-DIGIT NUMBERS X 2-DIGIT NUMBERS

11 worksheets
9 problems per sheet

Decimal Multiplication | 3-Digit Numbers X 2-Digit Numbers

Multiply.

1)
```
    441
x   .43
```

2)
```
   4.63
x   9.8
```

3)
```
    398
x   .51
```

4)
```
   62.4
x   2.1
```

5)
```
   1.97
x    45
```

6)
```
    399
x   .43
```

7)
```
    140
x   6.4
```

8)
```
    481
x   1.1
```

9)
```
   64.8
x   7.9
```

Decimal Multiplication | 3-Digit Numbers X 2-Digit Numbers

Multiply.

1)
$$
\begin{array}{r}
1.53 \\
\times\ 60 \\
\hline
\end{array}
$$

2)
$$
\begin{array}{r}
35.2 \\
\times\ 3.6 \\
\hline
\end{array}
$$

3)
$$
\begin{array}{r}
48.3 \\
\times\ 6.5 \\
\hline
\end{array}
$$

4)
$$
\begin{array}{r}
10.3 \\
\times\ .59 \\
\hline
\end{array}
$$

5)
$$
\begin{array}{r}
7.61 \\
\times\ 2.7 \\
\hline
\end{array}
$$

6)
$$
\begin{array}{r}
2.47 \\
\times\ 65 \\
\hline
\end{array}
$$

7)
$$
\begin{array}{r}
58.6 \\
\times\ 14 \\
\hline
\end{array}
$$

8)
$$
\begin{array}{r}
62.6 \\
\times\ 8.5 \\
\hline
\end{array}
$$

9)
$$
\begin{array}{r}
6.68 \\
\times\ 16 \\
\hline
\end{array}
$$

www.claymaze.com

Decimal Multiplication   3-Digit Numbers X 2-Digit Numbers

Multiply.

1)   393
   x .76
   _____

2)   6.91
   x 9.8
   _____

3)   13.8
   x .44
   _____

4)   2.57
   x 21
   _____

5)   8.85
   x 37
   _____

6)   71.5
   x 3.1
   _____

7)   6.22
   x 15
   _____

8)   9.15
   x 23
   _____

9)   9.31
   x 15
   _____

www.claymaze.com

Decimal Multiplication | 3-Digit Numbers X 2-Digit Numbers

Multiply.

1)
```
    882
x   .39
_____
```

2)
```
    735
x   .31
_____
```

3)
```
   6.71
x    58
_____
```

4)
```
    120
x   8.1
_____
```

5)
```
   8.58
x   1.8
_____
```

6)
```
   90.1
x   8.1
_____
```

7)
```
   9.53
x   7.5
_____
```

8)
```
   71.5
x   8.8
_____
```

9)
```
   9.59
x    76
_____
```

Decimal Multiplication | 3-Digit Numbers X 2-Digit Numbers

Multiply.

1)
$$12.9 \\ \times\ .84$$

2)
$$8.42 \\ \times\ 37$$

3)
$$2.52 \\ \times\ 20$$

4)
$$858 \\ \times\ .17$$

5)
$$8.41 \\ \times\ 70$$

6)
$$340 \\ \times\ 1.8$$

7)
$$741 \\ \times\ .53$$

8)
$$27.6 \\ \times\ .84$$

9)
$$93.2 \\ \times\ 6.2$$

Decimal Multiplication | 3-Digit Numbers X 2-Digit Numbers

Multiply.

1)
$$\begin{array}{r} 2.75 \\ \times\ 37 \\ \hline \end{array}$$

2)
$$\begin{array}{r} 822 \\ \times\ .51 \\ \hline \end{array}$$

3)
$$\begin{array}{r} 40.5 \\ \times\ 4.2 \\ \hline \end{array}$$

4)
$$\begin{array}{r} 6.53 \\ \times\ 47 \\ \hline \end{array}$$

5)
$$\begin{array}{r} 5.78 \\ \times\ 75 \\ \hline \end{array}$$

6)
$$\begin{array}{r} 729 \\ \times\ .15 \\ \hline \end{array}$$

7)
$$\begin{array}{r} 89.3 \\ \times\ .16 \\ \hline \end{array}$$

8)
$$\begin{array}{r} 483 \\ \times\ .72 \\ \hline \end{array}$$

9)
$$\begin{array}{r} 68.9 \\ \times\ 2.2 \\ \hline \end{array}$$

Decimal Multiplication | 3-Digit Numbers X 2-Digit Numbers

Multiply.

1)   3.09
   x 6.7
   _____

2)   47.2
   x 4.2
   _____

3)   5.11
   x 31
   _____

4)   9.21
   x 15
   _____

5)   5.08
   x 5.2
   _____

6)   6.46
   x 6.4
   _____

7)   559
   x .75
   _____

8)   15.3
   x .54
   _____

9)   871
   x .55
   _____

Name _____ Date _____

Decimal Multiplication | 3-Digit Numbers X 2-Digit Numbers

Multiply.

1)
```
  5.95
x 61
```

2)
```
  964
x .36
```

3)
```
  779
x .25
```

4)
```
  193
x .52
```

5)
```
  22.5
x 7.9
```

6)
```
  3.38
x 20
```

7)
```
  325
x .14
```

8)
```
  40.8
x .37
```

9)
```
  64.4
x 5.2
```

Decimal Multiplication | 3-Digit Numbers X 2-Digit Numbers

Multiply.

1) $\begin{array}{r} 2.45 \\ \times\ 8.5 \\ \hline \end{array}$

2) $\begin{array}{r} 29.2 \\ \times\ 6.7 \\ \hline \end{array}$

3) $\begin{array}{r} 622 \\ \times\ .74 \\ \hline \end{array}$

4) $\begin{array}{r} 7.96 \\ \times\ 20 \\ \hline \end{array}$

5) $\begin{array}{r} 58.2 \\ \times\ .39 \\ \hline \end{array}$

6) $\begin{array}{r} 42.4 \\ \times\ 3.4 \\ \hline \end{array}$

7) $\begin{array}{r} 8.28 \\ \times\ 51 \\ \hline \end{array}$

8) $\begin{array}{r} 3.92 \\ \times\ 3.1 \\ \hline \end{array}$

9) $\begin{array}{r} 297 \\ \times\ .54 \\ \hline \end{array}$

Decimal Multiplication | 3-Digit Numbers X 2-Digit Numbers

Multiply.

1)
```
    251
x   .78
```

2)
```
   2.87
x    28
```

3)
```
   70.4
x   4.3
```

4)
```
    875
x   .85
```

5)
```
   28.6
x    32
```

6)
```
    316
x   .74
```

7)
```
   83.9
x   .15
```

8)
```
   46.1
x   9.5
```

9)
```
    218
x   4.3
```

Decimal Multiplication | 3-Digit Numbers X 2-Digit Numbers

Multiply.

1)   72.3
   x 4.4
   _____

2)   397
   x   .67
   _____

3)   32.1
   x 2.5
   _____

4)   849
   x   .24
   _____

5)   2.33
   x   12
   _____

6)   39.8
   x   .33
   _____

7)   8.22
   x   57
   _____

8)   1.18
   x 4.4
   _____

9)   965
   x   .31
   _____

SECTION

DECIMAL DIVISION WITH 3-DIGIT NUMBERS

11 worksheets
16 problems per sheet

Decimal Division with 3-Digit Numbers

Divide.

1) $2 \overline{)\, 2.72\,}$ 2) $6 \overline{)\, 4.38\,}$ 3) $8 \overline{)\, 8.64\,}$ 4) $5 \overline{)\, 2.75\,}$

5) $3 \overline{)\, 2.34\,}$ 6) $4 \overline{)\, 6.72\,}$ 7) $3 \overline{)\, 8.25\,}$ 8) $7 \overline{)\, 8.96\,}$

9) $5 \overline{)\, 4.85\,}$ 10) $2 \overline{)\, 8.96\,}$ 11) $9 \overline{)\, 7.56\,}$ 12) $4 \overline{)\, 7.32\,}$

13) $3 \overline{)\, 2.16\,}$ 14) $6 \overline{)\, 8.76\,}$ 15) $2 \overline{)\, 8.22\,}$ 16) $8 \overline{)\, 6.64\,}$

Name _____ Date _____

Divide.

1) $4\overline{)1.48}$ 2) $3\overline{)1.92}$ 3) $7\overline{)4.83}$ 4) $2\overline{)1.66}$

5) $6\overline{)4.32}$ 6) $2\overline{)8.96}$ 7) $9\overline{)4.05}$ 8) $3\overline{)9.66}$

9) $2\overline{)1.82}$ 10) $5\overline{)8.25}$ 11) $4\overline{)7.92}$ 12) $5\overline{)3.75}$

13) $7\overline{)6.44}$ 14) $3\overline{)2.04}$ 15) $2\overline{)4.68}$ 16) $3\overline{)1.83}$

Decimal Division with 3-Digit Numbers

Divide.

1) $9 \overline{)1.44}$ 2) $8 \overline{)4.72}$ 3) $7 \overline{)5.32}$ 4) $6 \overline{)5.16}$

5) $4 \overline{)2.56}$ 6) $9 \overline{)3.87}$ 7) $6 \overline{)9.78}$ 8) $4 \overline{)9.56}$

9) $2 \overline{)9.28}$ 10) $8 \overline{)3.68}$ 11) $3 \overline{)4.62}$ 12) $5 \overline{)3.05}$

13) $7 \overline{)6.79}$ 14) $2 \overline{)6.98}$ 15) $4 \overline{)1.28}$ 16) $2 \overline{)3.74}$

Decimal Division with 3-Digit Numbers

Divide.

1) $7\overline{)4.06}$ 2) $9\overline{)1.08}$ 3) $4\overline{)1.04}$ 4) $2\overline{)1.46}$

5) $3\overline{)2.25}$ 6) $8\overline{)3.92}$ 7) $5\overline{)4.85}$ 8) $6\overline{)1.02}$

9) $2\overline{)5.64}$ 10) $7\overline{)1.05}$ 11) $2\overline{)3.24}$ 12) $4\overline{)3.44}$

13) $7\overline{)5.53}$ 14) $5\overline{)8.85}$ 15) $3\overline{)8.22}$ 16) $5\overline{)2.45}$

Decimal Division | with 3-Digit Numbers

Divide.

1) $8\overline{)6.32}$ 2) $3\overline{)4.92}$ 3) $5\overline{)4.35}$ 4) $2\overline{)4.82}$

5) $9\overline{)2.43}$ 6) $6\overline{)7.98}$ 7) $2\overline{)4.98}$ 8) $7\overline{)5.67}$

9) $3\overline{)8.91}$ 10) $7\overline{)6.02}$ 11) $4\overline{)2.48}$ 12) $9\overline{)2.79}$

13) $8\overline{)2.24}$ 14) $9\overline{)8.19}$ 15) $2\overline{)2.14}$ 16) $3\overline{)1.98}$

Decimal Division   with 3-Digit Numbers

Divide.

1) $7\overline{)4.13}$ 2) $6\overline{)6.84}$ 3) $8\overline{)4.48}$ 4) $2\overline{)1.54}$

5) $9\overline{)4.41}$ 6) $3\overline{)3.57}$ 7) $5\overline{)1.45}$ 8) $6\overline{)1.44}$

9) $2\overline{)7.02}$ 10) $4\overline{)3.56}$ 11) $8\overline{)3.36}$ 12) $2\overline{)9.04}$

13) $6\overline{)4.62}$ 14) $7\overline{)2.03}$ 15) $3\overline{)5.85}$ 16) $4\overline{)3.24}$

Decimal Division   with 3-Digit Numbers

Divide.

1) $7\overline{)5.18}$ 2) $3\overline{)3.93}$ 3) $8\overline{)3.12}$ 4) $9\overline{)4.95}$

5) $3\overline{)1.44}$ 6) $2\overline{)2.36}$ 7) $6\overline{)3.54}$ 8) $3\overline{)2.52}$

9) $8\overline{)8.32}$ 10) $6\overline{)2.16}$ 11) $8\overline{)7.68}$ 12) $9\overline{)7.92}$

13) $6\overline{)5.22}$ 14) $2\overline{)2.94}$ 15) $4\overline{)1.72}$ 16) $5\overline{)4.25}$

Decimal Division with 3-Digit Numbers

Divide.

1) $4\overline{)1.92}$ 2) $7\overline{)4.83}$ 3) $6\overline{)1.98}$ 4) $2\overline{)8.46}$

5) $3\overline{)9.81}$ 6) $5\overline{)2.75}$ 7) $2\overline{)4.32}$ 8) $7\overline{)4.41}$

9) $6\overline{)3.84}$ 10) $7\overline{)1.54}$ 11) $3\overline{)2.25}$ 12) $2\overline{)7.88}$

13) $9\overline{)4.32}$ 14) $2\overline{)4.16}$ 15) $4\overline{)1.04}$ 16) $8\overline{)5.52}$

Decimal Division with 3-Digit Numbers

Divide.

1) $7\overline{)6.79}$ 2) $6\overline{)3.54}$ 3) $2\overline{)1.72}$ 4) $4\overline{)5.32}$

5) $2\overline{)8.62}$ 6) $5\overline{)4.75}$ 7) $4\overline{)2.96}$ 8) $3\overline{)7.92}$

9) $9\overline{)1.53}$ 10) $4\overline{)2.68}$ 11) $2\overline{)6.18}$ 12) $5\overline{)2.75}$

13) $2\overline{)2.86}$ 14) $3\overline{)8.67}$ 15) $7\overline{)9.94}$ 16) $3\overline{)8.22}$

Decimal Division   with 3-Digit Numbers

Divide.

1) $8\overline{)4.64}$ 2) $4\overline{)8.92}$ 3) $9\overline{)6.57}$ 4) $2\overline{)1.58}$

5) $3\overline{)1.17}$ 6) $6\overline{)4.32}$ 7) $7\overline{)8.82}$ 8) $8\overline{)1.44}$

9) $7\overline{)2.31}$ 10) $2\overline{)5.82}$ 11) $5\overline{)2.05}$ 12) $9\overline{)7.83}$

13) $8\overline{)3.12}$ 14) $7\overline{)5.46}$ 15) $2\overline{)9.92}$ 16) $3\overline{)7.32}$

Decimal Division   with 3-Digit Numbers

Divide.

1) $2\overline{)8.08}$ 2) $4\overline{)8.04}$ 3) $6\overline{)9.36}$ 4) $4\overline{)9.68}$

5) $7\overline{)3.64}$ 6) $2\overline{)8.88}$ 7) $5\overline{)9.45}$ 8) $3\overline{)2.43}$

9) $8\overline{)1.92}$ 10) $9\overline{)8.64}$ 11) $8\overline{)1.44}$ 12) $6\overline{)7.74}$

13) $3\overline{)4.35}$ 14) $2\overline{)1.56}$ 15) $3\overline{)8.07}$ 16) $2\overline{)8.86}$

SECTION

DECIMAL DIVISION WITH DECIMAL DIVISORS

11 worksheets
9 problems per sheet

Decimal Division with Decimal Divisors

Divide. *(Hint: Shift the decimal to the right on both the divisor & the dividend.)*

1) $.4\overline{)16.08}$ 2) $.3\overline{)206.1}$ 3) $.6\overline{)25.74}$

4) $.5\overline{)333.5}$ 5) $.9\overline{)75.96}$ 6) $.7\overline{)66.71}$

7) $.3\overline{)17.91}$ 8) $.7\overline{)58.73}$ 9) $.3\overline{)21.39}$

Name _____ Date _____

Decimal Division with Decimal Divisors

Divide. *(Hint: Shift the decimal to the right on both the divisor & the dividend.)*

1) $.6\overline{)586.8}$

2) $.7\overline{)19.95}$

3) $.6\overline{)484.2}$

4) $.9\overline{)27.72}$

5) $.4\overline{)25.76}$

6) $.9\overline{)492.3}$

7) $.6\overline{)40.38}$

8) $.8\overline{)72.56}$

9) $.4\overline{)182.4}$

Decimal Division   with Decimal Divisors

Divide. *(Hint: Shift the decimal to the right on both the divisor & the dividend.)*

1) $.3\overline{)183.6}$ 2) $.7\overline{)27.58}$ 3) $.6\overline{)495.6}$

4) $.2\overline{)166.4}$ 5) $.3\overline{)28.68}$ 6) $.8\overline{)441.6}$

7) $.7\overline{)28.14}$ 8) $.5\overline{)216.5}$ 9) $.7\overline{)589.4}$

Name _____   Date _____

Decimal Division | with Decimal Divisors

Divide. *(Hint: Shift the decimal to the right on both the divisor & the dividend.)*

1) $.8\overline{)61.92}$

2) $.7\overline{)34.86}$

3) $.4\overline{)17.24}$

4) $.9\overline{)313.2}$

5) $.2\overline{)139.6}$

6) $.8\overline{)43.76}$

7) $.4\overline{)34.16}$

8) $.8\overline{)343.2}$

9) $.7\overline{)221.2}$

www.claymaze.com

Decimal Division with Decimal Divisors

Divide. *(Hint: Shift the decimal to the right on both the divisor & the dividend.)*

1) $.8\overline{)51.04}$ 2) $.2\overline{)19.12}$ 3) $.5\overline{)38.15}$

4) $.6\overline{)223.2}$ 5) $.7\overline{)13.58}$ 6) $.9\overline{)592.2}$

7) $.5\overline{)48.25}$ 8) $.9\overline{)20.61}$ 9) $.4\overline{)11.68}$

Decimal Division with Decimal Divisors

Divide. *(Hint: Shift the decimal to the right on both the divisor & the dividend.)*

1) $.7\overline{)533.4}$

2) $.9\overline{)416.7}$

3) $.6\overline{)223.8}$

4) $.3\overline{)22.89}$

5) $.8\overline{)67.52}$

6) $.7\overline{)51.73}$

7) $.5\overline{)244.5}$

8) $.4\overline{)125.6}$

9) $.9\overline{)795.6}$

Decimal Division with Decimal Divisors

Divide. *(Hint: Shift the decimal to the right on both the divisor & the dividend.)*

1) $.6\overline{)51.84}$

2) $.2\overline{)10.18}$

3) $.3\overline{)15.93}$

4) $.7\overline{)59.92}$

5) $.8\overline{)523.2}$

6) $.7\overline{)32.76}$

7) $.6\overline{)18.24}$

8) $.4\overline{)38.04}$

9) $.3\overline{)180.6}$

Decimal Division   with Decimal Divisors

Divide. *(Hint: Shift the decimal to the right on both the divisor & the dividend.)*

1) $.8\overline{)39.12}$

2) $.3\overline{)188.7}$

3) $.7\overline{)50.61}$

4) $.6\overline{)558.6}$

5) $.2\overline{)169.4}$

6) $.4\overline{)29.76}$

7) $.8\overline{)738.4}$

8) $.3\overline{)250.5}$

9) $.6\overline{)311.4}$

Name _____ Date _____

Decimal Division with Decimal Divisors

Divide. *(Hint: Shift the decimal to the right on both the divisor & the dividend.)*

1) $.3\overline{)239.4}$

2) $.2\overline{)15.32}$

3) $.5\overline{)25.45}$

4) $.2\overline{)11.32}$

5) $.6\overline{)46.26}$

6) $.9\overline{)206.1}$

7) $.6\overline{)17.46}$

8) $.8\overline{)443.2}$

9) $.3\overline{)295.8}$

Decimal Division   with Decimal Divisors

Divide. *(Hint: Shift the decimal to the right on both the divisor & the dividend.)*

1) $.7\overline{)10.43}$

2) $.8\overline{)787.2}$

3) $.9\overline{)68.94}$

4) $.6\overline{)16.32}$

5) $.7\overline{)61.53}$

6) $.8\overline{)76.16}$

7) $.5\overline{)41.95}$

8) $.6\overline{)26.04}$

9) $.9\overline{)81.36}$

Decimal Division with Decimal Divisors

Divide. *(Hint: Shift the decimal to the right on both the divisor & the dividend.)*

1) $.8\overline{)59.28}$

2) $.9\overline{)883.8}$

3) $.5\overline{)19.65}$

4) $.4\overline{)12.28}$

5) $.3\overline{)21.99}$

6) $.8\overline{)237.6}$

7) $.6\overline{)250.2}$

8) $.9\overline{)485.1}$

9) $.7\overline{)38.78}$

SECTION

16

ROUNDING WITH DECIMALS

11 worksheets
36 problems per sheet

Name _____   Date _____

Rounding with Decimals

Round to the nearest whole number.

1) 30.701 _____   2) 23.824 _____   3) 11.395 _____

4) 41.221 _____   5) 76.657 _____   6) 69.514 _____

7) 99.604 _____   8) 65.244 _____   9) 23.724 _____

10) 12.318 _____   11) 50.086 _____   12) 41.251 _____

Round to the nearest tenths.

13) 15.674 _____   14) 89.826 _____   15) 85.872 _____

16) 59.489 _____   17) 73.227 _____   18) 43.318 _____

19) 81.125 _____   20) 15.288 _____   21) 79.468 _____

22) 45.863 _____   23) 72.748 _____   24) 30.372 _____

Round to the nearest hundreths.

25) 42.572 _____   26) 96.219 _____   27) 22.368 _____

28) 31.384 _____   29) 13.014 _____   30) 93.231 _____

31) 81.916 _____   32) 36.819 _____   33) 89.725 _____

34) 16.475 _____   35) 29.172 _____   36) 19.007 _____

www.claymaze.com

Rounding with Decimals

Round to the nearest whole number.

1) 87.886 _____   2) 30.599 _____   3) 44.823 _____

4) 14.204 _____   5) 33.221 _____   6) 91.872 _____

7) 68.251 _____   8) 66.784 _____   9) 90.883 _____

10) 46.941 _____   11) 58.711 _____   12) 43.844 _____

Round to the nearest tenths.

13) 67.068 _____   14) 11.357 _____   15) 41.793 _____

16) 86.271 _____   17) 67.803 _____   18) 80.576 _____

19) 44.998 _____   20) 43.642 _____   21) 92.212 _____

22) 38.481 _____   23) 71.344 _____   24) 87.781 _____

Round to the nearest hundreths.

25) 50.429 _____   26) 18.387 _____   27) 47.001 _____

28) 96.195 _____   29) 28.434 _____   30) 34.027 _____

31) 34.877 _____   32) 57.622 _____   33) 42.596 _____

34) 64.892 _____   35) 40.299 _____   36) 37.814 _____

Rounding with Decimals

Round to the nearest whole number.

1) 56.132 _____   2) 15.828 _____   3) 20.443 _____

4) 83.984 _____   5) 93.271 _____   6) 78.407 _____

7) 23.315 _____   8) 64.102 _____   9) 81.204 _____

10) 21.478 _____   11) 92.647 _____   12) 50.936 _____

Round to the nearest tenths.

13) 97.365 _____   14) 95.054 _____   15) 77.034 _____

16) 84.018 _____   17) 69.136 _____   18) 26.452 _____

19) 37.339 _____   20) 47.617 _____   21) 42.516 _____

22) 47.977 _____   23) 27.018 _____   24) 22.597 _____

Round to the nearest hundreths.

25) 48.903 _____   26) 94.231 _____   27) 89.458 _____

28) 40.829 _____   29) 22.645 _____   30) 92.747 _____

31) 30.428 _____   32) 34.344 _____   33) 64.808 _____

34) 57.118 _____   35) 12.423 _____   36) 48.962 _____

Rounding with Decimals

Round to the nearest whole number.

1) 40.478 _____   2) 31.385 _____   3) 43.288 _____

4) 33.002 _____   5) 61.557 _____   6) 45.428 _____

7) 66.179 _____   8) 44.742 _____   9) 15.222 _____

10) 30.737 _____   11) 47.781 _____   12) 38.653 _____

Round to the nearest tenths.

13) 54.386 _____   14) 35.893 _____   15) 78.923 _____

16) 25.639 _____   17) 27.185 _____   18) 90.692 _____

19) 23.695 _____   20) 61.997 _____   21) 75.385 _____

22) 23.442 _____   23) 82.156 _____   24) 94.202 _____

Round to the nearest hundreths.

25) 67.175 _____   26) 26.722 _____   27) 83.421 _____

28) 25.872 _____   29) 80.054 _____   30) 30.211 _____

31) 65.616 _____   32) 71.269 _____   33) 65.944 _____

34) 79.005 _____   35) 83.538 _____   36) 81.295 _____

Name _____   Date _____

Rounding with Decimals

Round to the nearest whole number.

1) 62.884 _____   2) 50.892 _____   3) 59.848 _____

4) 54.566 _____   5) 50.215 _____   6) 65.357 _____

7) 61.395 _____   8) 40.402 _____   9) 35.437 _____

10) 10.663 _____   11) 53.542 _____   12) 92.979 _____

Round to the nearest tenths.

13) 51.758 _____   14) 38.365 _____   15) 65.378 _____

16) 84.377 _____   17) 55.734 _____   18) 68.565 _____

19) 28.036 _____   20) 56.933 _____   21) 65.375 _____

22) 25.279 _____   23) 76.535 _____   24) 30.983 _____

Round to the nearest hundreths.

25) 75.704 _____   26) 81.714 _____   27) 88.938 _____

28) 11.448 _____   29) 57.354 _____   30) 16.644 _____

31) 60.283 _____   32) 18.616 _____   33) 61.802 _____

34) 21.787 _____   35) 25.614 _____   36) 82.793 _____

www.claymaze.com

Rounding with Decimals

Round to the nearest whole number.

1) 72.702 _____   2) 80.635 _____   3) 26.219 _____

4) 99.148 _____   5) 27.026 _____   6) 88.196 _____

7) 89.701 _____   8) 97.679 _____   9) 33.772 _____

10) 14.314 _____   11) 47.919 _____   12) 82.297 _____

Round to the nearest tenths.

13) 82.812 _____   14) 14.002 _____   15) 54.598 _____

16) 51.948 _____   17) 63.251 _____   18) 65.032 _____

19) 23.029 _____   20) 85.052 _____   21) 73.701 _____

22) 95.516 _____   23) 21.829 _____   24) 90.394 _____

Round to the nearest hundreths.

25) 39.122 _____   26) 44.317 _____   27) 27.935 _____

28) 47.432 _____   29) 82.051 _____   30) 57.245 _____

31) 61.534 _____   32) 78.465 _____   33) 32.051 _____

34) 85.404 _____   35) 45.927 _____   36) 61.646 _____

www.claymaze.com

Rounding with Decimals

Round to the nearest whole number.

1) 62.776 _____   2) 62.363 _____   3) 55.647 _____

4) 42.263 _____   5) 74.483 _____   6) 43.341 _____

7) 81.252 _____   8) 41.254 _____   9) 43.918 _____

10) 99.325 _____   11) 40.019 _____   12) 87.816 _____

Round to the nearest tenths.

13) 44.105 _____   14) 87.979 _____   15) 65.253 _____

16) 76.281 _____   17) 14.017 _____   18) 48.433 _____

19) 42.299 _____   20) 58.402 _____   21) 79.592 _____

22) 20.081 _____   23) 44.132 _____   24) 80.639 _____

Round to the nearest hundreths.

25) 68.959 _____   26) 28.719 _____   27) 65.491 _____

28) 81.147 _____   29) 90.338 _____   30) 23.039 _____

31) 60.343 _____   32) 45.374 _____   33) 12.488 _____

34) 97.537 _____   35) 77.894 _____   36) 55.262 _____

Rounding with Decimals

Round to the nearest whole number.

1) 28.186 _____   2) 34.121 _____   3) 29.555 _____

4) 57.693 _____   5) 60.522 _____   6) 21.879 _____

7) 30.688 _____   8) 39.644 _____   9) 43.777 _____

10) 84.016 _____   11) 91.631 _____   12) 27.684 _____

Round to the nearest tenths.

13) 97.286 _____   14) 56.336 _____   15) 33.641 _____

16) 62.862 _____   17) 31.098 _____   18) 68.635 _____

19) 35.939 _____   20) 28.847 _____   21) 78.474 _____

22) 16.002 _____   23) 38.685 _____   24) 12.502 _____

Round to the nearest hundreths.

25) 10.929 _____   26) 36.057 _____   27) 41.643 _____

28) 69.098 _____   29) 55.923 _____   30) 49.616 _____

31) 82.057 _____   32) 16.346 _____   33) 58.184 _____

34) 77.598 _____   35) 32.929 _____   36) 30.502 _____

Name _____ Date _____

Rounding with Decimals

Round to the nearest whole number.

1) 14.645 _____ 2) 99.218 _____ 3) 99.625 _____

4) 60.864 _____ 5) 92.275 _____ 6) 98.301 _____

7) 27.828 _____ 8) 51.845 _____ 9) 15.227 _____

10) 44.571 _____ 11) 81.959 _____ 12) 54.752 _____

Round to the nearest tenths.

13) 58.907 _____ 14) 61.268 _____ 15) 51.853 _____

16) 81.079 _____ 17) 21.034 _____ 18) 68.338 _____

19) 12.579 _____ 20) 85.898 _____ 21) 62.252 _____

22) 20.641 _____ 23) 53.552 _____ 24) 52.118 _____

Round to the nearest hundreths.

25) 34.423 _____ 26) 47.206 _____ 27) 28.432 _____

28) 87.172 _____ 29) 83.668 _____ 30) 16.129 _____

31) 18.188 _____ 32) 39.977 _____ 33) 71.064 _____

34) 17.174 _____ 35) 46.183 _____ 36) 45.196 _____

www.claymaze.com

Rounding with Decimals

Round to the nearest whole number.

1) 15.196 _____   2) 53.683 _____   3) 35.428 _____

4) 60.122 _____   5) 95.519 _____   6) 64.136 _____

7) 53.438 _____   8) 62.452 _____   9) 69.217 _____

10) 91.371 _____   11) 33.925 _____   12) 98.149 _____

Round to the nearest tenths.

13) 83.353 _____   14) 97.948 _____   15) 16.595 _____

16) 94.683 _____   17) 11.145 _____   18) 26.101 _____

19) 10.211 _____   20) 41.376 _____   21) 37.861 _____

22) 82.017 _____   23) 38.964 _____   24) 56.551 _____

Round to the nearest hundreths.

25) 41.401 _____   26) 52.421 _____   27) 45.832 _____

28) 64.293 _____   29) 53.322 _____   30) 83.534 _____

31) 80.723 _____   32) 91.982 _____   33) 78.599 _____

34) 26.791 _____   35) 97.257 _____   36) 87.245 _____

Rounding with Decimals

Round to the nearest whole number.

1) 46.628 _____   2) 20.435 _____   3) 23.737 _____

4) 86.238 _____   5) 81.123 _____   6) 48.736 _____

7) 75.085 _____   8) 33.954 _____   9) 24.842 _____

10) 54.171 _____   11) 22.807 _____   12) 24.012 _____

Round to the nearest tenths.

13) 35.578 _____   14) 91.847 _____   15) 60.749 _____

16) 33.837 _____   17) 89.916 _____   18) 67.798 _____

19) 38.622 _____   20) 28.089 _____   21) 57.596 _____

22) 82.435 _____   23) 34.804 _____   24) 73.235 _____

Round to the nearest hundreths.

25) 82.602 _____   26) 49.308 _____   27) 79.374 _____

28) 88.307 _____   29) 57.694 _____   30) 78.384 _____

31) 10.372 _____   32) 61.091 _____   33) 67.121 _____

34) 40.751 _____   35) 56.959 _____   36) 26.919 _____

SECTION

DECIMALS AND PERCENTAGES

11 worksheets
22 problems per sheet

Decimals and Percentages

Write the decimals as percentages.

1) .68 _____   2) .78 _____   3) .85 _____   4) .4 _____

5) .61 _____   6) .97 _____   7) .41 _____   8) .07 _____

Write the percentages as decimals.

9) 38% _____   10) 55% _____   11) 70% _____   12) 17% _____

13) 8% _____   14) 15% _____   15) 33% _____   16) 36% _____

Calculate the percentages.

17) 47% of 54   18) 32% of 91   19) 92% of 94

20) 86% of 86   21) 68% of 35   22) 89% of 58

Decimals and Percentages

Write the decimals as percentages.

1) .9 _____   2) .19 _____   3) .36 _____   4) .71 _____

5) .94 _____   6) .38 _____   7) .41 _____   8) .97 _____

Write the percentages as decimals.

9) 40% _____   10) 92% _____   11) 65% _____   12) 14% _____

13) 12% _____   14) 85% _____   15) 27% _____   16) 5% _____

Calculate the percentages.

17) 97% of 19   18) 50% of 15   19) 39% of 39

20) 48% of 77   21) 82% of 49   22) 27% of 53

Decimals and Percentages

Write the decimals as percentages.

1) .38 _____   2) .73 _____   3) .23 _____   4) .37 _____

5) .49 _____   6) .86 _____   7) .02 _____   8) .31 _____

Write the percentages as decimals.

9) 54% _____   10) 2% _____   11) 43% _____   12) 14% _____

13) 40% _____   14) 44% _____   15) 88% _____   16) 52% _____

Calculate the percentages.

17) 62% of 62   18) 33% of 64   19) 55% of 72

20) 87% of 43   21) 65% of 85   22) 54% of 89

Decimals and Percentages

Write the decimals as percentages.

1) .35 _____   2) .41 _____   3) .44 _____   4) .67 _____

5) .58 _____   6) .43 _____   7) .66 _____   8) .15 _____

Write the percentages as decimals.

9) 69% _____   10) 28% _____   11) 51% _____   12) 52% _____

13) 95% _____   14) 96% _____   15) 49% _____   16) 32% _____

Calculate the percentages.

17) 17% of 63   18) 49% of 96   19) 2% of 38

20) 93% of 34   21) 95% of 49   22) 85% of 60

Decimals and Percentages

Write the decimals as percentages.

1) .95 _____   2) .51 _____   3) .46 _____   4) .42 _____

5) .29 _____   6) .55 _____   7) .03 _____   8) .53 _____

Write the percentages as decimals.

9) 36% _____   10) 18% _____   11) 87% _____   12) 43% _____

13) 51% _____   14) 36% _____   15) 14% _____   16) 75% _____

Calculate the percentages.

17) 37% of 86   18) 66% of 87   19) 30% of 90

20) 98% of 82   21) 95% of 45   22) 9% of 35

Decimals and Percentages

Write the decimals as percentages.

1) .79 _____   2) .27 _____   3) .23 _____   4) .39 _____

5) .85 _____   6) .49 _____   7) .56 _____   8) .64 _____

Write the percentages as decimals.

9) 46% _____   10) 48% _____   11) 74% _____   12) 28% _____

13) 52% _____   14) 96% _____   15) 10% _____   16) 45% _____

Calculate the percentages.

17) 54% of 97   18) 26% of 69   19) 27% of 80

20) 28% of 15   21) 33% of 32   22) 76% of 10

Decimals and Percentages

Write the decimals as percentages.

1) .97 _____   2) .91 _____   3) .74 _____   4) .96 _____

5) .04 _____   6) .27 _____   7) .25 _____   8) .17 _____

Write the percentages as decimals.

9) 77% _____   10) 82% _____   11) 9% _____   12) 93% _____

13) 71% _____   14) 42% _____   15) 64% _____   16) 46% _____

Calculate the percentages.

17) 5% of 83   18) 50% of 57   19) 21% of 20

20) 11% of 80   21) 1% of 11   22) 24% of 75

Decimals and Percentages

Write the decimals as percentages.

1) .85 _____   2) .63 _____   3) .13 _____   4) .93 _____

5) .49 _____   6) .45 _____   7) .61 _____   8) .22 _____

Write the percentages as decimals.

9) 60% _____   10) 95% _____   11) 79% _____   12) 88% _____

13) 4% _____   14) 1% _____   15) 46% _____   16) 20% _____

Calculate the percentages.

17) 84% of 95   18) 11% of 28   19) 46% of 76

20) 55% of 59   21) 3% of 49   22) 13% of 59

Decimals and Percentages

Write the decimals as percentages.

1) .6 _____   2) .54 _____   3) .3 _____   4) .32 _____

5) .82 _____   6) .41 _____   7) .86 _____   8) .15 _____

Write the percentages as decimals.

9) 41% _____   10) 72% _____   11) 79% _____   12) 88% _____

13) 25% _____ 14) 12% _____   15) 61% _____   16) 19% _____

Calculate the percentages.

17) 85% of 23   18) 63% of 65   19) 71% of 64

20) 43% of 99   21) 49% of 40   22) 18% of 70

www.claymaze.com

Decimals and Percentages

Write the decimals as percentages.

1) .94 _____   2) .41 _____   3) .76 _____   4) .07 _____

5) .38 _____   6) .93 _____   7) .78 _____   8) .8 _____

Write the percentages as decimals.

9) 32% _____   10) 37% _____   11) 82% _____   12) 46% _____

13) 96% _____   14) 57% _____   15) 65% _____   16) 35% _____

Calculate the percentages.

17) 75% of 76   18) 3% of 17   19) 84% of 15

20) 11% of 17   21) 21% of 87   22) 8% of 34

Decimals and Percentages

Write the decimals as percentages.

1) .69 _____   2) .37 _____   3) .73 _____   4) .28 _____

5) .7 _____   6) .11 _____   7) .46 _____   8) .03 _____

Write the percentages as decimals.

9) 88% _____   10) 31% _____   11) 35% _____   12) 16% _____

13) 39% _____   14) 50% _____   15) 42% _____   16) 98% _____

Calculate the percentages.

17) 50% of 68   18) 8% of 55   19) 68% of 45

20) 27% of 11   21) 43% of 10   22) 52% of 21

SOLUTIONS

SOLUTIONS TO PROBLEMS

Sections 1 - 17

Simplify.

1) $\dfrac{8}{88} = \dfrac{1}{11}$ 2) $\dfrac{28}{32} = \dfrac{7}{8}$ 3) $\dfrac{21}{28} = \dfrac{3}{4}$

4) $\dfrac{16}{20} = \dfrac{4}{5}$ 5) $\dfrac{14}{18} = \dfrac{7}{9}$ 6) $\dfrac{28}{44} = \dfrac{7}{11}$

7) $\dfrac{30}{54} = \dfrac{5}{9}$ 8) $\dfrac{49}{70} = \dfrac{7}{10}$ 9) $\dfrac{16}{40} = \dfrac{2}{5}$

10) $\dfrac{40}{55} = \dfrac{8}{11}$ 11) $\dfrac{6}{8} = \dfrac{3}{4}$ 12) $\dfrac{4}{8} = \dfrac{1}{2}$

13) $\dfrac{20}{28} = \dfrac{5}{7}$ 14) $\dfrac{18}{48} = \dfrac{3}{8}$ 15) $\dfrac{18}{75} = \dfrac{6}{25}$

16) $\dfrac{5}{10} = \dfrac{1}{2}$ 17) $\dfrac{3}{6} = \dfrac{1}{2}$ 18) $\dfrac{10}{12} = \dfrac{5}{6}$

19) $\dfrac{8}{100} = \dfrac{2}{25}$ 20) $\dfrac{20}{25} = \dfrac{4}{5}$ 21) $\dfrac{5}{50} = \dfrac{1}{10}$

Simplify.

1) $\dfrac{56}{63} = \dfrac{8}{9}$ 2) $\dfrac{10}{35} = \dfrac{2}{7}$ 3) $\dfrac{48}{54} = \dfrac{8}{9}$

4) $\dfrac{25}{35} = \dfrac{5}{7}$ 5) $\dfrac{21}{70} = \dfrac{3}{10}$ 6) $\dfrac{12}{18} = \dfrac{2}{3}$

7) $\dfrac{12}{27} = \dfrac{4}{9}$ 8) $\dfrac{6}{33} = \dfrac{2}{11}$ 9) $\dfrac{4}{20} = \dfrac{1}{5}$

10) $\dfrac{15}{25} = \dfrac{3}{5}$ 11) $\dfrac{35}{56} = \dfrac{5}{8}$ 12) $\dfrac{32}{100} = \dfrac{8}{25}$

13) $\dfrac{3}{21} = \dfrac{1}{7}$ 14) $\dfrac{16}{88} = \dfrac{2}{11}$ 15) $\dfrac{21}{49} = \dfrac{3}{7}$

16) $\dfrac{8}{12} = \dfrac{2}{3}$ 17) $\dfrac{8}{32} = \dfrac{1}{4}$ 18) $\dfrac{18}{45} = \dfrac{2}{5}$

19) $\dfrac{35}{55} = \dfrac{7}{11}$ 20) $\dfrac{5}{10} = \dfrac{1}{2}$ 21) $\dfrac{6}{75} = \dfrac{2}{25}$

Simplify.

1) $\dfrac{4}{8} = \dfrac{1}{2}$ 2) $\dfrac{18}{22} = \dfrac{9}{11}$ 3) $\dfrac{10}{12} = \dfrac{5}{6}$

4) $\dfrac{4}{6} = \dfrac{2}{3}$ 5) $\dfrac{35}{56} = \dfrac{5}{8}$ 6) $\dfrac{6}{10} = \dfrac{3}{5}$

7) $\dfrac{2}{4} = \dfrac{1}{2}$ 8) $\dfrac{18}{30} = \dfrac{3}{5}$ 9) $\dfrac{9}{33} = \dfrac{3}{11}$

10) $\dfrac{20}{24} = \dfrac{5}{6}$ 11) $\dfrac{18}{20} = \dfrac{9}{10}$ 12) $\dfrac{18}{24} = \dfrac{3}{4}$

13) $\dfrac{24}{44} = \dfrac{6}{11}$ 14) $\dfrac{64}{72} = \dfrac{8}{9}$ 15) $\dfrac{56}{77} = \dfrac{8}{11}$

16) $\dfrac{36}{42} = \dfrac{6}{7}$ 17) $\dfrac{24}{32} = \dfrac{3}{4}$ 18) $\dfrac{35}{45} = \dfrac{7}{9}$

19) $\dfrac{8}{12} = \dfrac{2}{3}$ 20) $\dfrac{12}{42} = \dfrac{2}{7}$ 21) $\dfrac{24}{75} = \dfrac{8}{25}$

Simplify.

1) $\dfrac{14}{22} = \dfrac{7}{11}$ 2) $\dfrac{14}{50} = \dfrac{7}{25}$ 3) $\dfrac{10}{15} = \dfrac{2}{3}$

4) $\dfrac{9}{54} = \dfrac{1}{6}$ 5) $\dfrac{12}{20} = \dfrac{3}{5}$ 6) $\dfrac{27}{75} = \dfrac{9}{25}$

7) $\dfrac{3}{75} = \dfrac{1}{25}$ 8) $\dfrac{2}{4} = \dfrac{1}{2}$ 9) $\dfrac{24}{50} = \dfrac{12}{25}$

10) $\dfrac{5}{15} = \dfrac{1}{3}$ 11) $\dfrac{15}{55} = \dfrac{3}{11}$ 12) $\dfrac{45}{72} = \dfrac{5}{8}$

13) $\dfrac{36}{45} = \dfrac{4}{5}$ 14) $\dfrac{16}{28} = \dfrac{4}{7}$ 15) $\dfrac{5}{55} = \dfrac{1}{11}$

16) $\dfrac{7}{77} = \dfrac{1}{11}$ 17) $\dfrac{18}{30} = \dfrac{3}{5}$ 18) $\dfrac{28}{36} = \dfrac{7}{9}$

19) $\dfrac{45}{81} = \dfrac{5}{9}$ 20) $\dfrac{7}{49} = \dfrac{1}{7}$ 21) $\dfrac{10}{25} = \dfrac{2}{5}$

Simplify.

1) $\dfrac{28}{44} = \dfrac{7}{11}$ 2) $\dfrac{24}{75} = \dfrac{8}{25}$ 3) $\dfrac{15}{21} = \dfrac{5}{7}$

4) $\dfrac{12}{100} = \dfrac{3}{25}$ 5) $\dfrac{8}{40} = \dfrac{1}{5}$ 6) $\dfrac{12}{50} = \dfrac{6}{25}$

7) $\dfrac{6}{9} = \dfrac{2}{3}$ 8) $\dfrac{6}{21} = \dfrac{2}{7}$ 9) $\dfrac{16}{24} = \dfrac{2}{3}$

10) $\dfrac{6}{12} = \dfrac{1}{2}$ 11) $\dfrac{32}{40} = \dfrac{4}{5}$ 12) $\dfrac{24}{40} = \dfrac{3}{5}$

13) $\dfrac{3}{15} = \dfrac{1}{5}$ 14) $\dfrac{40}{72} = \dfrac{5}{9}$ 15) $\dfrac{12}{33} = \dfrac{4}{11}$

16) $\dfrac{63}{90} = \dfrac{7}{10}$ 17) $\dfrac{7}{35} = \dfrac{1}{5}$ 18) $\dfrac{21}{24} = \dfrac{7}{8}$

19) $\dfrac{42}{54} = \dfrac{7}{9}$ 20) $\dfrac{27}{75} = \dfrac{9}{25}$ 21) $\dfrac{12}{18} = \dfrac{2}{3}$

Simplify.

1) $\dfrac{36}{100} = \dfrac{9}{25}$ 2) $\dfrac{18}{22} = \dfrac{9}{11}$ 3) $\dfrac{6}{24} = \dfrac{1}{4}$

4) $\dfrac{5}{40} = \dfrac{1}{8}$ 5) $\dfrac{32}{36} = \dfrac{8}{9}$ 6) $\dfrac{2}{4} = \dfrac{1}{2}$

7) $\dfrac{16}{28} = \dfrac{4}{7}$ 8) $\dfrac{9}{90} = \dfrac{1}{10}$ 9) $\dfrac{6}{15} = \dfrac{2}{5}$

10) $\dfrac{8}{18} = \dfrac{4}{9}$ 11) $\dfrac{3}{15} = \dfrac{1}{5}$ 12) $\dfrac{36}{42} = \dfrac{6}{7}$

13) $\dfrac{5}{50} = \dfrac{1}{10}$ 14) $\dfrac{14}{22} = \dfrac{7}{11}$ 15) $\dfrac{4}{12} = \dfrac{1}{3}$

16) $\dfrac{12}{50} = \dfrac{6}{25}$ 17) $\dfrac{4}{8} = \dfrac{1}{2}$ 18) $\dfrac{24}{36} = \dfrac{2}{3}$

19) $\dfrac{18}{21} = \dfrac{6}{7}$ 20) $\dfrac{16}{50} = \dfrac{8}{25}$ 21) $\dfrac{15}{20} = \dfrac{3}{4}$

www.claymaze.com

PAGE: 8

Simplify.

1) $\frac{12}{30} = \frac{2}{5}$ 2) $\frac{6}{12} = \frac{1}{2}$ 3) $\frac{48}{66} = \frac{8}{11}$

4) $\frac{7}{28} = \frac{1}{4}$ 5) $\frac{12}{18} = \frac{2}{3}$ 6) $\frac{5}{20} = \frac{1}{4}$

7) $\frac{27}{33} = \frac{9}{11}$ 8) $\frac{15}{25} = \frac{3}{5}$ 9) $\frac{12}{54} = \frac{2}{9}$

10) $\frac{8}{20} = \frac{2}{5}$ 11) $\frac{8}{14} = \frac{4}{7}$ 12) $\frac{24}{75} = \frac{8}{25}$

13) $\frac{9}{81} = \frac{1}{9}$ 14) $\frac{10}{22} = \frac{5}{11}$ 15) $\frac{45}{63} = \frac{5}{7}$

16) $\frac{16}{24} = \frac{2}{3}$ 17) $\frac{20}{25} = \frac{4}{5}$ 18) $\frac{35}{40} = \frac{7}{8}$

19) $\frac{6}{48} = \frac{1}{8}$ 20) $\frac{5}{10} = \frac{1}{2}$ 21) $\frac{14}{63} = \frac{2}{9}$

PAGE: 9

Simplify.

1) $\frac{4}{6} = \frac{2}{3}$ 2) $\frac{18}{30} = \frac{3}{5}$ 3) $\frac{40}{55} = \frac{8}{11}$

4) $\frac{6}{22} = \frac{3}{11}$ 5) $\frac{20}{24} = \frac{5}{6}$ 6) $\frac{6}{24} = \frac{1}{4}$

7) $\frac{9}{45} = \frac{1}{5}$ 8) $\frac{9}{33} = \frac{3}{11}$ 9) $\frac{18}{81} = \frac{2}{9}$

10) $\frac{15}{27} = \frac{5}{9}$ 11) $\frac{54}{60} = \frac{9}{10}$ 12) $\frac{27}{45} = \frac{3}{5}$

13) $\frac{3}{33} = \frac{1}{11}$ 14) $\frac{9}{18} = \frac{1}{2}$ 15) $\frac{9}{54} = \frac{1}{6}$

16) $\frac{7}{14} = \frac{1}{2}$ 17) $\frac{4}{50} = \frac{2}{25}$ 18) $\frac{32}{72} = \frac{4}{9}$

19) $\frac{16}{100} = \frac{4}{25}$ 20) $\frac{6}{36} = \frac{1}{6}$ 21) $\frac{32}{40} = \frac{4}{5}$

PAGE: 10

Simplify.

1) $\frac{2}{6} = \frac{1}{3}$ 2) $\frac{10}{12} = \frac{5}{6}$ 3) $\frac{25}{40} = \frac{5}{8}$

4) $\frac{7}{35} = \frac{1}{5}$ 5) $\frac{21}{77} = \frac{3}{11}$ 6) $\frac{7}{21} = \frac{1}{3}$

7) $\frac{72}{80} = \frac{9}{10}$ 8) $\frac{10}{35} = \frac{2}{7}$ 9) $\frac{4}{18} = \frac{2}{9}$

10) $\frac{15}{25} = \frac{3}{5}$ 11) $\frac{27}{36} = \frac{3}{4}$ 12) $\frac{3}{9} = \frac{1}{3}$

13) $\frac{45}{55} = \frac{9}{11}$ 14) $\frac{24}{30} = \frac{4}{5}$ 15) $\frac{27}{90} = \frac{3}{10}$

16) $\frac{10}{15} = \frac{2}{3}$ 17) $\frac{72}{81} = \frac{8}{9}$ 18) $\frac{16}{50} = \frac{8}{25}$

19) $\frac{56}{80} = \frac{7}{10}$ 20) $\frac{27}{75} = \frac{9}{25}$ 21) $\frac{4}{6} = \frac{2}{3}$

PAGE: 11

Simplify.

1) $\frac{4}{10} = \frac{2}{5}$ 2) $\frac{30}{54} = \frac{5}{9}$ 3) $\frac{25}{50} = \frac{1}{2}$

4) $\frac{4}{8} = \frac{1}{2}$ 5) $\frac{8}{40} = \frac{1}{5}$ 6) $\frac{15}{20} = \frac{3}{4}$

7) $\frac{14}{21} = \frac{2}{3}$ 8) $\frac{6}{8} = \frac{3}{4}$ 9) $\frac{18}{42} = \frac{3}{7}$

10) $\frac{4}{14} = \frac{2}{7}$ 11) $\frac{64}{88} = \frac{8}{11}$ 12) $\frac{9}{81} = \frac{1}{9}$

13) $\frac{72}{88} = \frac{9}{11}$ 14) $\frac{32}{40} = \frac{4}{5}$ 15) $\frac{10}{16} = \frac{5}{8}$

16) $\frac{15}{18} = \frac{5}{6}$ 17) $\frac{9}{63} = \frac{1}{7}$ 18) $\frac{15}{27} = \frac{5}{9}$

19) $\frac{20}{44} = \frac{5}{11}$ 20) $\frac{8}{32} = \frac{1}{4}$ 21) $\frac{14}{35} = \frac{2}{5}$

PAGE: 12

Simplify.

1) $\frac{8}{18} = \frac{4}{9}$ 2) $\frac{24}{80} = \frac{3}{10}$ 3) $\frac{16}{56} = \frac{2}{7}$

4) $\frac{27}{75} = \frac{9}{25}$ 5) $\frac{7}{14} = \frac{1}{2}$ 6) $\frac{8}{22} = \frac{4}{11}$

7) $\frac{4}{36} = \frac{1}{9}$ 8) $\frac{9}{54} = \frac{1}{6}$ 9) $\frac{6}{12} = \frac{1}{2}$

10) $\frac{4}{12} = \frac{1}{3}$ 11) $\frac{15}{33} = \frac{5}{11}$ 12) $\frac{49}{63} = \frac{7}{9}$

13) $\frac{25}{75} = \frac{1}{3}$ 14) $\frac{4}{32} = \frac{1}{8}$ 15) $\frac{42}{56} = \frac{3}{4}$

16) $\frac{63}{70} = \frac{9}{10}$ 17) $\frac{35}{40} = \frac{7}{8}$ 18) $\frac{15}{27} = \frac{5}{9}$

19) $\frac{4}{10} = \frac{2}{5}$ 20) $\frac{10}{18} = \frac{5}{9}$ 21) $\frac{15}{20} = \frac{3}{4}$

PAGE: 14

Complete the equivalent fractions.

1) $\frac{4}{8} = \frac{32}{64}$ 2) $\frac{5}{11} = \frac{45}{99}$ 3) $\frac{8}{10} = \frac{56}{70}$

4) $\frac{9}{11} = \frac{36}{44}$ 5) $\frac{6}{8} = \frac{54}{72}$ 6) $\frac{5}{9} = \frac{35}{63}$

7) $\frac{8}{100} = \frac{16}{200}$ 8) $\frac{8}{10} = \frac{40}{50}$ 9) $\frac{9}{12} = \frac{18}{24}$

10) $\frac{4}{8} = \frac{16}{32}$ 11) $\frac{8}{11} = \frac{72}{99}$ 12) $\frac{8}{9} = \frac{16}{18}$

13) $\frac{5}{7} = \frac{25}{35}$ 14) $\frac{6}{12} = \frac{18}{36}$ 15) $\frac{9}{11} = \frac{54}{66}$

16) $\frac{8}{12} = \frac{24}{36}$ 17) $\frac{8}{11} = \frac{56}{77}$ 18) $\frac{4}{8} = \frac{8}{16}$

19) $\frac{5}{100} = \frac{20}{400}$ 20) $\frac{7}{9} = \frac{14}{18}$ 21) $\frac{9}{10} = \frac{36}{40}$

www.claymaze.com

Complete the equivalent fractions.

1) $\frac{7}{8} = \frac{21}{24}$ 2) $\frac{5}{11} = \frac{25}{55}$ 3) $\frac{7}{9} = \frac{21}{27}$

4) $\frac{9}{11} = \frac{72}{88}$ 5) $\frac{6}{8} = \frac{36}{48}$ 6) $\frac{9}{100} = \frac{18}{200}$

7) $\frac{7}{12} = \frac{28}{48}$ 8) $\frac{9}{25} = \frac{18}{50}$ 9) $\frac{7}{8} = \frac{35}{40}$

10) $\frac{5}{6} = \frac{10}{12}$ 11) $\frac{6}{7} = \frac{24}{28}$ 12) $\frac{4}{25} = \frac{8}{50}$

13) $\frac{5}{8} = \frac{40}{64}$ 14) $\frac{7}{25} = \frac{21}{75}$ 15) $\frac{7}{100} = \frac{14}{200}$

16) $\frac{9}{12} = \frac{27}{36}$ 17) $\frac{6}{7} = \frac{12}{14}$ 18) $\frac{4}{8} = \frac{36}{72}$

19) $\frac{6}{100} = \frac{12}{200}$ 20) $\frac{8}{10} = \frac{40}{50}$ 21) $\frac{9}{11} = \frac{36}{44}$

Complete the equivalent fractions.

1) $\frac{4}{100} = \frac{12}{300}$ 2) $\frac{9}{10} = \frac{18}{20}$ 3) $\frac{8}{25} = \frac{32}{100}$

4) $\frac{7}{9} = \frac{14}{18}$ 5) $\frac{9}{25} = \frac{36}{100}$ 6) $\frac{9}{100} = \frac{36}{400}$

7) $\frac{9}{25} = \frac{18}{50}$ 8) $\frac{4}{12} = \frac{12}{36}$ 9) $\frac{9}{11} = \frac{27}{33}$

10) $\frac{4}{6} = \frac{8}{12}$ 11) $\frac{5}{8} = \frac{45}{72}$ 12) $\frac{5}{100} = \frac{20}{400}$

13) $\frac{6}{9} = \frac{48}{72}$ 14) $\frac{9}{100} = \frac{27}{300}$ 15) $\frac{7}{12} = \frac{14}{24}$

16) $\frac{9}{10} = \frac{81}{90}$ 17) $\frac{5}{6} = \frac{25}{30}$ 18) $\frac{9}{10} = \frac{63}{70}$

19) $\frac{6}{7} = \frac{48}{56}$ 20) $\frac{7}{10} = \frac{42}{60}$ 21) $\frac{6}{12} = \frac{12}{24}$

Complete the equivalent fractions.

1) $\frac{4}{12} = \frac{12}{36}$ 2) $\frac{9}{11} = \frac{63}{77}$ 3) $\frac{6}{7} = \frac{18}{21}$

4) $\frac{6}{9} = \frac{54}{81}$ 5) $\frac{9}{25} = \frac{18}{50}$ 6) $\frac{8}{100} = \frac{32}{400}$

7) $\frac{7}{10} = \frac{63}{90}$ 8) $\frac{8}{11} = \frac{40}{55}$ 9) $\frac{8}{10} = \frac{64}{80}$

10) $\frac{7}{11} = \frac{14}{22}$ 11) $\frac{4}{6} = \frac{8}{12}$ 12) $\frac{5}{8} = \frac{30}{48}$

13) $\frac{5}{10} = \frac{35}{70}$ 14) $\frac{5}{12} = \frac{15}{36}$ 15) $\frac{7}{100} = \frac{21}{300}$

16) $\frac{6}{11} = \frac{36}{66}$ 17) $\frac{9}{25} = \frac{36}{100}$ 18) $\frac{6}{9} = \frac{42}{63}$

19) $\frac{7}{9} = \frac{56}{72}$ 20) $\frac{8}{10} = \frac{56}{70}$ 21) $\frac{8}{25} = \frac{32}{100}$

Complete the equivalent fractions.

1) $\frac{7}{12} = \frac{14}{24}$ 2) $\frac{7}{25} = \frac{21}{75}$ 3) $\frac{4}{7} = \frac{24}{42}$

4) $\frac{6}{8} = \frac{18}{24}$ 5) $\frac{9}{11} = \frac{81}{99}$ 6) $\frac{4}{8} = \frac{20}{40}$

7) $\frac{5}{6} = \frac{40}{48}$ 8) $\frac{8}{12} = \frac{16}{24}$ 9) $\frac{6}{11} = \frac{54}{99}$

10) $\frac{8}{9} = \frac{48}{54}$ 11) $\frac{6}{10} = \frac{36}{60}$ 12) $\frac{4}{8} = \frac{32}{64}$

13) $\frac{6}{100} = \frac{12}{200}$ 14) $\frac{6}{11} = \frac{12}{22}$ 15) $\frac{8}{25} = \frac{32}{100}$

16) $\frac{4}{7} = \frac{16}{28}$ 17) $\frac{4}{12} = \frac{8}{24}$ 18) $\frac{7}{100} = \frac{28}{400}$

19) $\frac{5}{9} = \frac{45}{81}$ 20) $\frac{7}{25} = \frac{14}{50}$ 21) $\frac{4}{7} = \frac{20}{35}$

Complete the equivalent fractions.

1) $\frac{6}{8} = \frac{18}{24}$ 2) $\frac{5}{7} = \frac{40}{56}$ 3) $\frac{9}{10} = \frac{72}{80}$

4) $\frac{8}{100} = \frac{16}{200}$ 5) $\frac{7}{25} = \frac{14}{50}$ 6) $\frac{5}{11} = \frac{45}{99}$

7) $\frac{8}{10} = \frac{40}{50}$ 8) $\frac{6}{100} = \frac{18}{300}$ 9) $\frac{4}{9} = \frac{16}{36}$

10) $\frac{8}{11} = \frac{64}{88}$ 11) $\frac{8}{25} = \frac{16}{50}$ 12) $\frac{6}{11} = \frac{24}{44}$

13) $\frac{7}{8} = \frac{28}{32}$ 14) $\frac{9}{10} = \frac{81}{90}$ 15) $\frac{7}{12} = \frac{28}{48}$

16) $\frac{5}{100} = \frac{15}{300}$ 17) $\frac{5}{25} = \frac{20}{100}$ 18) $\frac{5}{11} = \frac{10}{22}$

19) $\frac{4}{12} = \frac{12}{36}$ 20) $\frac{6}{9} = \frac{36}{54}$ 21) $\frac{9}{25} = \frac{27}{75}$

Complete the equivalent fractions.

1) $\frac{7}{8} = \frac{28}{32}$ 2) $\frac{4}{25} = \frac{12}{75}$ 3) $\frac{4}{5} = \frac{8}{10}$

4) $\frac{4}{9} = \frac{8}{18}$ 5) $\frac{5}{10} = \frac{45}{90}$ 6) $\frac{7}{9} = \frac{56}{72}$

7) $\frac{6}{11} = \frac{42}{77}$ 8) $\frac{9}{12} = \frac{18}{24}$ 9) $\frac{5}{25} = \frac{20}{100}$

10) $\frac{6}{10} = \frac{48}{80}$ 11) $\frac{5}{11} = \frac{35}{77}$ 12) $\frac{8}{9} = \frac{32}{36}$

13) $\frac{6}{9} = \frac{18}{27}$ 14) $\frac{6}{7} = \frac{30}{35}$ 15) $\frac{9}{11} = \frac{63}{77}$

16) $\frac{8}{25} = \frac{32}{100}$ 17) $\frac{5}{100} = \frac{20}{400}$ 18) $\frac{5}{9} = \frac{45}{81}$

19) $\frac{8}{100} = \frac{24}{300}$ 20) $\frac{6}{25} = \frac{12}{50}$ 21) $\frac{5}{12} = \frac{10}{24}$

www.claymaze.com

Complete the equivalent fractions.

1) $\frac{7}{11} = \frac{56}{88}$ 2) $\frac{9}{25} = \frac{36}{100}$ 3) $\frac{8}{10} = \frac{72}{90}$

4) $\frac{4}{100} = \frac{8}{200}$ 5) $\frac{6}{12} = \frac{12}{24}$ 6) $\frac{9}{100} = \frac{36}{400}$

7) $\frac{4}{25} = \frac{8}{50}$ 8) $\frac{6}{11} = \frac{54}{99}$ 9) $\frac{6}{9} = \frac{12}{18}$

10) $\frac{4}{9} = \frac{32}{72}$ 11) $\frac{8}{100} = \frac{16}{200}$ 12) $\frac{7}{25} = \frac{21}{75}$

13) $\frac{6}{25} = \frac{12}{50}$ 14) $\frac{9}{10} = \frac{63}{70}$ 15) $\frac{8}{9} = \frac{32}{36}$

16) $\frac{5}{9} = \frac{15}{27}$ 17) $\frac{4}{12} = \frac{12}{36}$ 18) $\frac{8}{100} = \frac{32}{400}$

19) $\frac{8}{11} = \frac{40}{55}$ 20) $\frac{6}{100} = \frac{18}{300}$ 21) $\frac{6}{25} = \frac{18}{75}$

Complete the equivalent fractions.

1) $\frac{8}{10} = \frac{32}{40}$ 2) $\frac{4}{5} = \frac{36}{45}$ 3) $\frac{4}{9} = \frac{28}{63}$

4) $\frac{7}{25} = \frac{21}{75}$ 5) $\frac{7}{9} = \frac{35}{45}$ 6) $\frac{9}{10} = \frac{36}{40}$

7) $\frac{7}{10} = \frac{14}{20}$ 8) $\frac{5}{100} = \frac{10}{200}$ 9) $\frac{4}{5} = \frac{8}{10}$

10) $\frac{4}{100} = \frac{12}{300}$ 11) $\frac{4}{7} = \frac{12}{21}$ 12) $\frac{4}{8} = \frac{24}{48}$

13) $\frac{6}{12} = \frac{12}{24}$ 14) $\frac{5}{6} = \frac{30}{36}$ 15) $\frac{8}{10} = \frac{48}{60}$

16) $\frac{6}{25} = \frac{18}{75}$ 17) $\frac{9}{10} = \frac{18}{20}$ 18) $\frac{9}{12} = \frac{36}{48}$

19) $\frac{5}{6} = \frac{20}{24}$ 20) $\frac{8}{12} = \frac{24}{36}$ 21) $\frac{4}{100} = \frac{8}{200}$

Complete the equivalent fractions.

1) $\frac{7}{12} = \frac{14}{24}$ 2) $\frac{7}{10} = \frac{49}{70}$ 3) $\frac{4}{5} = \frac{16}{20}$

4) $\frac{5}{11} = \frac{35}{77}$ 5) $\frac{4}{100} = \frac{16}{400}$ 6) $\frac{5}{25} = \frac{20}{100}$

7) $\frac{5}{100} = \frac{20}{400}$ 8) $\frac{6}{12} = \frac{12}{24}$ 9) $\frac{8}{100} = \frac{24}{300}$

10) $\frac{8}{11} = \frac{32}{44}$ 11) $\frac{9}{25} = \frac{27}{75}$ 12) $\frac{4}{12} = \frac{12}{36}$

13) $\frac{5}{9} = \frac{35}{63}$ 14) $\frac{7}{100} = \frac{14}{200}$ 15) $\frac{9}{11} = \frac{54}{66}$

16) $\frac{5}{8} = \frac{15}{24}$ 17) $\frac{5}{6} = \frac{10}{12}$ 18) $\frac{6}{100} = \frac{24}{400}$

19) $\frac{6}{7} = \frac{24}{28}$ 20) $\frac{5}{8} = \frac{30}{48}$ 21) $\frac{7}{10} = \frac{14}{20}$

Complete the equivalent fractions.

1) $\frac{4}{12} = \frac{16}{48}$ 2) $\frac{5}{11} = \frac{20}{44}$ 3) $\frac{5}{25} = \frac{20}{100}$

4) $\frac{6}{25} = \frac{12}{50}$ 5) $\frac{5}{9} = \frac{25}{45}$ 6) $\frac{6}{12} = \frac{12}{24}$

7) $\frac{9}{10} = \frac{54}{60}$ 8) $\frac{6}{12} = \frac{18}{36}$ 9) $\frac{9}{100} = \frac{18}{200}$

10) $\frac{6}{9} = \frac{36}{54}$ 11) $\frac{8}{11} = \frac{24}{33}$ 12) $\frac{5}{9} = \frac{30}{54}$

13) $\frac{7}{12} = \frac{14}{24}$ 14) $\frac{5}{7} = \frac{35}{49}$ 15) $\frac{9}{12} = \frac{18}{24}$

16) $\frac{5}{7} = \frac{45}{63}$ 17) $\frac{7}{11} = \frac{49}{77}$ 18) $\frac{4}{6} = \frac{32}{48}$

19) $\frac{6}{10} = \frac{42}{70}$ 20) $\frac{8}{9} = \frac{64}{72}$ 21) $\frac{5}{10} = \frac{15}{30}$

Convert the mixed numbers to improper fractions.

1) $8\frac{1}{12} = \frac{97}{12}$ 2) $1\frac{8}{11} = \frac{19}{11}$ 3) $4\frac{6}{8} = \frac{19}{4}$

4) $5\frac{3}{4} = \frac{23}{4}$ 5) $4\frac{8}{9} = \frac{44}{9}$ 6) $6\frac{9}{12} = \frac{27}{4}$

7) $3\frac{8}{9} = \frac{35}{9}$ 8) $7\frac{3}{11} = \frac{80}{11}$ 9) $4\frac{6}{10} = \frac{23}{5}$

10) $2\frac{6}{7} = \frac{20}{7}$ 11) $3\frac{1}{9} = \frac{28}{9}$ 12) $2\frac{3}{7} = \frac{17}{7}$

13) $5\frac{3}{9} = \frac{16}{3}$ 14) $1\frac{3}{7} = \frac{10}{7}$ 15) $3\frac{6}{11} = \frac{39}{11}$

16) $6\frac{7}{10} = \frac{67}{10}$ 17) $8\frac{1}{8} = \frac{65}{8}$ 18) $5\frac{7}{10} = \frac{57}{10}$

19) $3\frac{2}{5} = \frac{17}{5}$ 20) $5\frac{4}{10} = \frac{27}{5}$ 21) $7\frac{5}{7} = \frac{54}{7}$

Convert the mixed numbers to improper fractions.

1) $4\frac{6}{11} = \frac{50}{11}$ 2) $5\frac{6}{7} = \frac{41}{7}$ 3) $1\frac{6}{10} = \frac{8}{5}$

4) $6\frac{5}{9} = \frac{59}{9}$ 5) $3\frac{4}{12} = \frac{10}{3}$ 6) $7\frac{1}{7} = \frac{50}{7}$

7) $3\frac{1}{10} = \frac{31}{10}$ 8) $5\frac{2}{3} = \frac{17}{3}$ 9) $4\frac{7}{11} = \frac{51}{11}$

10) $2\frac{2}{12} = \frac{13}{6}$ 11) $1\frac{3}{4} = \frac{7}{4}$ 12) $2\frac{4}{9} = \frac{22}{9}$

13) $8\frac{2}{9} = \frac{74}{9}$ 14) $5\frac{7}{10} = \frac{57}{10}$ 15) $4\frac{1}{5} = \frac{21}{5}$

16) $5\frac{4}{8} = \frac{11}{2}$ 17) $7\frac{7}{12} = \frac{91}{12}$ 18) $5\frac{1}{10} = \frac{51}{10}$

19) $3\frac{8}{9} = \frac{35}{9}$ 20) $4\frac{6}{7} = \frac{34}{7}$ 21) $1\frac{1}{8} = \frac{9}{8}$

www.claymaze.com

Convert the mixed numbers to improper fractions and simplify.

1) $6\frac{1}{3} = \frac{19}{3}$ 2) $1\frac{1}{12} = \frac{13}{12}$ 3) $3\frac{3}{9} = \frac{10}{3}$

4) $7\frac{2}{8} = \frac{29}{4}$ 5) $5\frac{4}{11} = \frac{59}{11}$ 6) $1\frac{4}{8} = \frac{3}{2}$

7) $3\frac{2}{10} = \frac{16}{5}$ 8) $2\frac{1}{3} = \frac{7}{3}$ 9) $8\frac{8}{12} = \frac{26}{3}$

10) $7\frac{8}{11} = \frac{85}{11}$ 11) $3\frac{1}{2} = \frac{7}{2}$ 12) $7\frac{3}{9} = \frac{22}{3}$

13) $1\frac{2}{9} = \frac{11}{9}$ 14) $6\frac{1}{4} = \frac{25}{4}$ 15) $5\frac{1}{6} = \frac{31}{6}$

16) $5\frac{5}{7} = \frac{40}{7}$ 17) $7\frac{7}{12} = \frac{91}{12}$ 18) $3\frac{7}{11} = \frac{40}{11}$

19) $7\frac{5}{9} = \frac{68}{9}$ 20) $5\frac{2}{7} = \frac{37}{7}$ 21) $1\frac{3}{5} = \frac{8}{5}$

Convert the mixed numbers to improper fractions and simplify.

1) $2\frac{1}{11} = \frac{23}{11}$ 2) $4\frac{6}{7} = \frac{34}{7}$ 3) $2\frac{7}{11} = \frac{29}{11}$

4) $4\frac{3}{10} = \frac{43}{10}$ 5) $6\frac{8}{11} = \frac{74}{11}$ 6) $3\frac{7}{9} = \frac{34}{9}$

7) $3\frac{8}{11} = \frac{41}{11}$ 8) $4\frac{3}{6} = \frac{9}{2}$ 9) $1\frac{5}{12} = \frac{17}{12}$

10) $7\frac{6}{10} = \frac{38}{5}$ 11) $6\frac{7}{8} = \frac{55}{8}$ 12) $8\frac{7}{11} = \frac{95}{11}$

13) $6\frac{6}{8} = \frac{27}{4}$ 14) $2\frac{5}{11} = \frac{27}{11}$ 15) $5\frac{4}{9} = \frac{49}{9}$

16) $4\frac{5}{7} = \frac{33}{7}$ 17) $6\frac{6}{10} = \frac{33}{5}$ 18) $4\frac{5}{11} = \frac{49}{11}$

19) $8\frac{6}{9} = \frac{26}{3}$ 20) $5\frac{6}{7} = \frac{41}{7}$ 21) $3\frac{4}{6} = \frac{11}{3}$

Convert the mixed numbers to improper fractions and simplify.

1) $1\frac{8}{12} = \frac{5}{3}$ 2) $2\frac{1}{11} = \frac{23}{11}$ 3) $8\frac{6}{8} = \frac{35}{4}$

4) $8\frac{8}{11} = \frac{96}{11}$ 5) $3\frac{7}{9} = \frac{34}{9}$ 6) $5\frac{9}{12} = \frac{23}{4}$

7) $2\frac{2}{3} = \frac{8}{3}$ 8) $4\frac{4}{5} = \frac{24}{5}$ 9) $8\frac{1}{2} = \frac{17}{2}$

10) $3\frac{3}{8} = \frac{27}{8}$ 11) $5\frac{1}{9} = \frac{46}{9}$ 12) $6\frac{3}{10} = \frac{63}{10}$

13) $5\frac{3}{12} = \frac{21}{4}$ 14) $7\frac{2}{11} = \frac{79}{11}$ 15) $3\frac{2}{7} = \frac{23}{7}$

16) $2\frac{9}{10} = \frac{29}{10}$ 17) $6\frac{9}{12} = \frac{27}{4}$ 18) $8\frac{9}{10} = \frac{89}{10}$

19) $8\frac{7}{8} = \frac{71}{8}$ 20) $1\frac{9}{10} = \frac{19}{10}$ 21) $6\frac{5}{11} = \frac{71}{11}$

Convert the mixed numbers to improper fractions and simplify.

1) $2\frac{7}{8} = \frac{23}{8}$ 2) $7\frac{6}{9} = \frac{23}{3}$ 3) $2\frac{7}{12} = \frac{31}{12}$

4) $4\frac{2}{7} = \frac{30}{7}$ 5) $1\frac{9}{10} = \frac{19}{10}$ 6) $6\frac{7}{9} = \frac{61}{9}$

7) $3\frac{6}{8} = \frac{15}{4}$ 8) $7\frac{1}{3} = \frac{22}{3}$ 9) $2\frac{2}{10} = \frac{11}{5}$

10) $4\frac{3}{10} = \frac{43}{10}$ 11) $2\frac{9}{11} = \frac{31}{11}$ 12) $5\frac{8}{9} = \frac{53}{9}$

13) $2\frac{8}{11} = \frac{30}{11}$ 14) $1\frac{3}{8} = \frac{11}{8}$ 15) $7\frac{4}{6} = \frac{23}{3}$

16) $1\frac{1}{4} = \frac{5}{4}$ 17) $8\frac{5}{6} = \frac{53}{6}$ 18) $4\frac{2}{4} = \frac{9}{2}$

19) $4\frac{9}{12} = \frac{19}{4}$ 20) $1\frac{7}{8} = \frac{15}{8}$ 21) $3\frac{1}{11} = \frac{34}{11}$

Convert the mixed numbers to improper fractions and simplify.

1) $4\frac{3}{9} = \frac{13}{3}$ 2) $5\frac{2}{5} = \frac{27}{5}$ 3) $2\frac{4}{6} = \frac{8}{3}$

4) $8\frac{1}{8} = \frac{65}{8}$ 5) $3\frac{3}{9} = \frac{10}{3}$ 6) $7\frac{7}{12} = \frac{91}{12}$

7) $2\frac{2}{9} = \frac{20}{9}$ 8) $1\frac{6}{7} = \frac{13}{7}$ 9) $6\frac{2}{3} = \frac{20}{3}$

10) $4\frac{6}{11} = \frac{50}{11}$ 11) $5\frac{7}{8} = \frac{47}{8}$ 12) $3\frac{6}{12} = \frac{7}{2}$

13) $1\frac{5}{7} = \frac{12}{7}$ 14) $2\frac{7}{11} = \frac{29}{11}$ 15) $6\frac{3}{8} = \frac{51}{8}$

16) $5\frac{2}{4} = \frac{11}{2}$ 17) $1\frac{6}{12} = \frac{3}{2}$ 18) $4\frac{2}{6} = \frac{13}{3}$

19) $2\frac{5}{11} = \frac{27}{11}$ 20) $3\frac{4}{9} = \frac{31}{9}$ 21) $6\frac{8}{11} = \frac{74}{11}$

Convert the mixed numbers to improper fractions and simplify.

1) $5\frac{3}{5} = \frac{28}{5}$ 2) $3\frac{8}{11} = \frac{41}{11}$ 3) $6\frac{9}{12} = \frac{27}{4}$

4) $3\frac{6}{11} = \frac{39}{11}$ 5) $2\frac{6}{9} = \frac{8}{3}$ 6) $8\frac{2}{10} = \frac{41}{5}$

7) $6\frac{4}{9} = \frac{58}{9}$ 8) $1\frac{5}{10} = \frac{3}{2}$ 9) $5\frac{9}{11} = \frac{64}{11}$

10) $5\frac{3}{4} = \frac{23}{4}$ 11) $3\frac{8}{9} = \frac{35}{9}$ 12) $2\frac{7}{12} = \frac{31}{12}$

13) $4\frac{9}{11} = \frac{53}{11}$ 14) $2\frac{2}{5} = \frac{12}{5}$ 15) $3\frac{9}{10} = \frac{39}{10}$

16) $3\frac{2}{4} = \frac{7}{2}$ 17) $2\frac{6}{11} = \frac{28}{11}$ 18) $1\frac{5}{8} = \frac{13}{8}$

19) $2\frac{9}{12} = \frac{11}{4}$ 20) $8\frac{1}{2} = \frac{17}{2}$ 21) $6\frac{8}{12} = \frac{20}{3}$

www.claymaze.com

Convert the mixed numbers to improper fractions.

1) $2\frac{4}{6} = \frac{8}{3}$
2) $7\frac{8}{12} = \frac{23}{3}$
3) $4\frac{4}{10} = \frac{22}{5}$
4) $4\frac{1}{9} = \frac{37}{9}$
5) $1\frac{6}{10} = \frac{8}{5}$
6) $7\frac{1}{5} = \frac{36}{5}$
7) $2\frac{1}{7} = \frac{15}{7}$
8) $6\frac{3}{8} = \frac{51}{8}$
9) $1\frac{4}{7} = \frac{11}{7}$
10) $5\frac{1}{11} = \frac{56}{11}$
11) $4\frac{9}{12} = \frac{19}{4}$
12) $6\frac{8}{10} = \frac{34}{5}$
13) $3\frac{2}{8} = \frac{13}{4}$
14) $6\frac{1}{11} = \frac{67}{11}$
15) $7\frac{1}{6} = \frac{43}{6}$
16) $4\frac{8}{11} = \frac{52}{11}$
17) $3\frac{5}{7} = \frac{26}{7}$
18) $8\frac{8}{10} = \frac{44}{5}$
19) $8\frac{5}{10} = \frac{17}{2}$
20) $5\frac{3}{9} = \frac{16}{3}$
21) $7\frac{1}{4} = \frac{29}{4}$

Convert the mixed numbers to improper fractions.

1) $5\frac{6}{12} = \frac{11}{2}$
2) $1\frac{8}{9} = \frac{17}{9}$
3) $3\frac{7}{10} = \frac{37}{10}$
4) $3\frac{7}{9} = \frac{34}{9}$
5) $4\frac{5}{10} = \frac{9}{2}$
6) $7\frac{4}{12} = \frac{22}{3}$
7) $6\frac{6}{7} = \frac{48}{7}$
8) $1\frac{6}{8} = \frac{7}{4}$
9) $4\frac{1}{4} = \frac{17}{4}$
10) $3\frac{4}{11} = \frac{37}{11}$
11) $4\frac{4}{10} = \frac{22}{5}$
12) $3\frac{1}{12} = \frac{37}{12}$
13) $7\frac{4}{7} = \frac{53}{7}$
14) $5\frac{3}{9} = \frac{16}{3}$
15) $4\frac{9}{10} = \frac{49}{10}$
16) $3\frac{8}{11} = \frac{41}{11}$
17) $4\frac{5}{12} = \frac{53}{12}$
18) $7\frac{1}{6} = \frac{43}{6}$
19) $7\frac{1}{7} = \frac{50}{7}$
20) $8\frac{6}{9} = \frac{26}{3}$
21) $6\frac{7}{12} = \frac{79}{12}$

Convert the mixed numbers to improper fractions.

1) $7\frac{3}{5} = \frac{38}{5}$
2) $5\frac{3}{12} = \frac{21}{4}$
3) $1\frac{8}{11} = \frac{19}{11}$
4) $4\frac{1}{12} = \frac{49}{12}$
5) $2\frac{4}{6} = \frac{8}{3}$
6) $8\frac{6}{10} = \frac{43}{5}$
7) $3\frac{5}{9} = \frac{32}{9}$
8) $5\frac{1}{12} = \frac{61}{12}$
9) $3\frac{2}{3} = \frac{11}{3}$
10) $8\frac{5}{11} = \frac{93}{11}$
11) $2\frac{4}{8} = \frac{5}{2}$
12) $8\frac{4}{5} = \frac{44}{5}$
13) $3\frac{7}{9} = \frac{34}{9}$
14) $8\frac{2}{12} = \frac{49}{6}$
15) $5\frac{3}{4} = \frac{23}{4}$
16) $5\frac{8}{12} = \frac{17}{3}$
17) $4\frac{5}{6} = \frac{29}{6}$
18) $1\frac{6}{12} = \frac{3}{2}$
19) $1\frac{3}{6} = \frac{3}{2}$
20) $6\frac{2}{4} = \frac{13}{2}$
21) $7\frac{7}{8} = \frac{63}{8}$

Convert the improper fractions to mixed numbers.

1) $\frac{23}{3} = 7\frac{2}{3}$
2) $\frac{50}{11} = 4\frac{6}{11}$
3) $\frac{28}{5} = 5\frac{3}{5}$
4) $\frac{49}{8} = 6\frac{1}{8}$
5) $\frac{15}{2} = 7\frac{1}{2}$
6) $\frac{41}{12} = 3\frac{5}{12}$
7) $\frac{17}{9} = 1\frac{8}{9}$
8) $\frac{48}{11} = 4\frac{4}{11}$
9) $\frac{25}{3} = 8\frac{1}{3}$
10) $\frac{13}{4} = 3\frac{1}{4}$
11) $\frac{52}{9} = 5\frac{7}{9}$
12) $\frac{25}{4} = 6\frac{1}{4}$
13) $\frac{9}{2} = 4\frac{1}{2}$
14) $\frac{19}{12} = 1\frac{7}{12}$
15) $\frac{30}{11} = 2\frac{8}{11}$
16) $\frac{17}{5} = 3\frac{2}{5}$
17) $\frac{13}{2} = 6\frac{1}{2}$
18) $\frac{53}{6} = 8\frac{5}{6}$
19) $\frac{23}{10} = 2\frac{3}{10}$
20) $\frac{55}{12} = 4\frac{7}{12}$
21) $\frac{71}{11} = 6\frac{5}{11}$

Convert the improper fractions to mixed numbers.

1) $\frac{42}{11} = 3\frac{9}{11}$
2) $\frac{25}{3} = 8\frac{1}{3}$
3) $\frac{37}{9} = 4\frac{1}{9}$
4) $\frac{76}{9} = 8\frac{4}{9}$
5) $\frac{83}{11} = 7\frac{6}{11}$
6) $\frac{26}{3} = 8\frac{2}{3}$
7) $\frac{22}{5} = 4\frac{2}{5}$
8) $\frac{13}{10} = 1\frac{3}{10}$
9) $\frac{84}{11} = 7\frac{7}{11}$
10) $\frac{63}{11} = 5\frac{8}{11}$
11) $\frac{14}{5} = 2\frac{4}{5}$
12) $\frac{58}{7} = 8\frac{2}{7}$
13) $\frac{22}{9} = 2\frac{4}{9}$
14) $\frac{17}{12} = 1\frac{5}{12}$
15) $\frac{8}{3} = 2\frac{2}{3}$
16) $\frac{9}{2} = 4\frac{1}{2}$
17) $\frac{67}{9} = 7\frac{4}{9}$
18) $\frac{21}{4} = 5\frac{1}{4}$
19) $\frac{69}{10} = 6\frac{9}{10}$
20) $\frac{65}{12} = 5\frac{5}{12}$
21) $\frac{13}{3} = 4\frac{1}{3}$

Convert the improper fractions to mixed numbers.

1) $\frac{7}{2} = 3\frac{1}{2}$
2) $\frac{23}{3} = 7\frac{2}{3}$
3) $\frac{9}{5} = 1\frac{4}{5}$
4) $\frac{4}{3} = 1\frac{1}{3}$
5) $\frac{13}{2} = 6\frac{1}{2}$
6) $\frac{25}{6} = 4\frac{1}{6}$
7) $\frac{67}{12} = 5\frac{7}{12}$
8) $\frac{60}{7} = 8\frac{4}{7}$
9) $\frac{89}{12} = 7\frac{5}{12}$
10) $\frac{11}{7} = 1\frac{4}{7}$
11) $\frac{19}{5} = 3\frac{4}{5}$
12) $\frac{20}{3} = 6\frac{2}{3}$
13) $\frac{17}{2} = 8\frac{1}{2}$
14) $\frac{11}{4} = 2\frac{3}{4}$
15) $\frac{80}{9} = 8\frac{8}{9}$
16) $\frac{17}{3} = 5\frac{2}{3}$
17) $\frac{3}{2} = 1\frac{1}{2}$
18) $\frac{33}{5} = 6\frac{3}{5}$
19) $\frac{9}{8} = 1\frac{1}{8}$
20) $\frac{22}{9} = 2\frac{4}{9}$
21) $\frac{15}{4} = 3\frac{3}{4}$

www.claymaze.com

PAGE: 41

Convert the improper fractions to mixed numbers.

1) $\frac{19}{10} = 1\frac{9}{10}$ 2) $\frac{60}{11} = 5\frac{5}{11}$ 3) $\frac{5}{2} = 2\frac{1}{2}$

4) $\frac{38}{9} = 4\frac{2}{9}$ 5) $\frac{4}{3} = 1\frac{1}{3}$ 6) $\frac{81}{11} = 7\frac{4}{11}$

7) $\frac{37}{6} = 6\frac{1}{6}$ 8) $\frac{31}{4} = 7\frac{3}{4}$ 9) $\frac{20}{3} = 6\frac{2}{3}$

10) $\frac{61}{11} = 5\frac{6}{11}$ 11) $\frac{59}{7} = 8\frac{3}{7}$ 12) $\frac{43}{6} = 7\frac{1}{6}$

13) $\frac{11}{6} = 1\frac{5}{6}$ 14) $\frac{13}{2} = 6\frac{1}{2}$ 15) $\frac{7}{3} = 2\frac{1}{3}$

16) $\frac{53}{7} = 7\frac{4}{7}$ 17) $\frac{17}{11} = 1\frac{6}{11}$ 18) $\frac{31}{6} = 5\frac{1}{6}$

19) $\frac{23}{9} = 2\frac{5}{9}$ 20) $\frac{45}{8} = 5\frac{5}{8}$ 21) $\frac{47}{11} = 4\frac{3}{11}$

PAGE: 42

Convert the improper fractions to mixed numbers.

1) $\frac{37}{5} = 7\frac{2}{5}$ 2) $\frac{79}{9} = 8\frac{7}{9}$ 3) $\frac{9}{4} = 2\frac{1}{4}$

4) $\frac{48}{11} = 4\frac{4}{11}$ 5) $\frac{38}{5} = 7\frac{3}{5}$ 6) $\frac{59}{11} = 5\frac{4}{11}$

7) $\frac{47}{8} = 5\frac{7}{8}$ 8) $\frac{30}{7} = 4\frac{2}{7}$ 9) $\frac{37}{10} = 3\frac{7}{10}$

10) $\frac{97}{11} = 8\frac{9}{11}$ 11) $\frac{63}{10} = 6\frac{3}{10}$ 12) $\frac{21}{8} = 2\frac{5}{8}$

13) $\frac{13}{8} = 1\frac{5}{8}$ 14) $\frac{25}{3} = 8\frac{1}{3}$ 15) $\frac{16}{9} = 1\frac{7}{9}$

16) $\frac{27}{7} = 3\frac{6}{7}$ 17) $\frac{6}{5} = 1\frac{1}{5}$ 18) $\frac{36}{11} = 3\frac{3}{11}$

19) $\frac{14}{3} = 4\frac{2}{3}$ 20) $\frac{58}{7} = 8\frac{2}{7}$ 21) $\frac{22}{3} = 7\frac{1}{3}$

PAGE: 43

Convert the improper fractions to mixed numbers.

1) $\frac{25}{9} = 2\frac{7}{9}$ 2) $\frac{3}{2} = 1\frac{1}{2}$ 3) $\frac{26}{3} = 8\frac{2}{3}$

4) $\frac{15}{4} = 3\frac{3}{4}$ 5) $\frac{27}{11} = 2\frac{5}{11}$ 6) $\frac{37}{9} = 4\frac{1}{9}$

7) $\frac{89}{12} = 7\frac{5}{12}$ 8) $\frac{27}{5} = 5\frac{2}{5}$ 9) $\frac{19}{6} = 3\frac{1}{6}$

10) $\frac{55}{8} = 6\frac{7}{8}$ 11) $\frac{14}{3} = 4\frac{2}{3}$ 12) $\frac{61}{8} = 7\frac{5}{8}$

13) $\frac{19}{5} = 3\frac{4}{5}$ 14) $\frac{18}{11} = 1\frac{7}{11}$ 15) $\frac{23}{4} = 5\frac{3}{4}$

16) $\frac{8}{7} = 1\frac{1}{7}$ 17) $\frac{23}{5} = 4\frac{3}{5}$ 18) $\frac{14}{9} = 1\frac{5}{9}$

19) $\frac{75}{11} = 6\frac{9}{11}$ 20) $\frac{17}{8} = 2\frac{1}{8}$ 21) $\frac{53}{11} = 4\frac{9}{11}$

PAGE: 44

Convert the improper fractions to mixed numbers.

1) $\frac{11}{3} = 3\frac{2}{3}$ 2) $\frac{80}{11} = 7\frac{3}{11}$ 3) $\frac{9}{2} = 4\frac{1}{2}$

4) $\frac{13}{2} = 6\frac{1}{2}$ 5) $\frac{37}{10} = 3\frac{7}{10}$ 6) $\frac{20}{11} = 1\frac{9}{11}$

7) $\frac{38}{9} = 4\frac{2}{9}$ 8) $\frac{85}{11} = 7\frac{8}{11}$ 9) $\frac{15}{4} = 3\frac{3}{4}$

10) $\frac{30}{11} = 2\frac{8}{11}$ 11) $\frac{67}{10} = 6\frac{7}{10}$ 12) $\frac{22}{5} = 4\frac{2}{5}$

13) $\frac{26}{3} = 8\frac{2}{3}$ 14) $\frac{11}{5} = 2\frac{1}{5}$ 15) $\frac{47}{9} = 5\frac{2}{9}$

16) $\frac{63}{8} = 7\frac{7}{8}$ 17) $\frac{69}{11} = 6\frac{3}{11}$ 18) $\frac{69}{8} = 8\frac{5}{8}$

19) $\frac{74}{9} = 8\frac{2}{9}$ 20) $\frac{27}{7} = 3\frac{6}{7}$ 21) $\frac{8}{5} = 1\frac{3}{5}$

PAGE: 45

Convert the improper fractions to mixed numbers.

1) $\frac{5}{2} = 2\frac{1}{2}$ 2) $\frac{34}{5} = 6\frac{4}{5}$ 3) $\frac{30}{11} = 2\frac{8}{11}$

4) $\frac{39}{11} = 3\frac{6}{11}$ 5) $\frac{19}{4} = 4\frac{3}{4}$ 6) $\frac{71}{8} = 8\frac{7}{8}$

7) $\frac{7}{4} = 1\frac{3}{4}$ 8) $\frac{19}{5} = 3\frac{4}{5}$ 9) $\frac{61}{9} = 6\frac{7}{9}$

10) $\frac{41}{12} = 3\frac{5}{12}$ 11) $\frac{53}{8} = 6\frac{5}{8}$ 12) $\frac{31}{12} = 2\frac{7}{12}$

13) $\frac{29}{11} = 2\frac{7}{11}$ 14) $\frac{11}{2} = 5\frac{1}{2}$ 15) $\frac{27}{4} = 6\frac{3}{4}$

16) $\frac{41}{9} = 4\frac{5}{9}$ 17) $\frac{90}{11} = 8\frac{2}{11}$ 18) $\frac{9}{2} = 4\frac{1}{2}$

19) $\frac{87}{10} = 8\frac{7}{10}$ 20) $\frac{39}{5} = 7\frac{4}{5}$ 21) $\frac{11}{10} = 1\frac{1}{10}$

PAGE: 46

Convert the improper fractions to mixed numbers.

1) $\frac{68}{11} = 6\frac{2}{11}$ 2) $\frac{43}{12} = 3\frac{7}{12}$ 3) $\frac{9}{5} = 1\frac{4}{5}$

4) $\frac{5}{3} = 1\frac{2}{3}$ 5) $\frac{19}{4} = 4\frac{3}{4}$ 6) $\frac{7}{2} = 3\frac{1}{2}$

7) $\frac{23}{5} = 4\frac{3}{5}$ 8) $\frac{61}{10} = 6\frac{1}{10}$ 9) $\frac{31}{12} = 2\frac{7}{12}$

10) $\frac{14}{11} = 1\frac{3}{11}$ 11) $\frac{5}{2} = 2\frac{1}{2}$ 12) $\frac{14}{3} = 4\frac{2}{3}$

13) $\frac{27}{4} = 6\frac{3}{4}$ 14) $\frac{71}{9} = 7\frac{8}{9}$ 15) $\frac{57}{7} = 8\frac{1}{7}$

16) $\frac{21}{10} = 2\frac{1}{10}$ 17) $\frac{16}{3} = 5\frac{1}{3}$ 18) $\frac{63}{10} = 6\frac{3}{10}$

19) $\frac{25}{3} = 8\frac{1}{3}$ 20) $\frac{25}{4} = 6\frac{1}{4}$ 21) $\frac{21}{5} = 4\frac{1}{5}$

Convert the improper fractions to mixed numbers.

1) $\frac{74}{11} = 6\frac{8}{11}$ 2) $\frac{10}{3} = 3\frac{1}{3}$ 3) $\frac{71}{9} = 7\frac{8}{9}$

4) $\frac{55}{12} = 4\frac{7}{12}$ 5) $\frac{89}{10} = 8\frac{9}{10}$ 6) $\frac{12}{5} = 2\frac{2}{5}$

7) $\frac{33}{4} = 8\frac{1}{4}$ 8) $\frac{83}{11} = 7\frac{6}{11}$ 9) $\frac{59}{10} = 5\frac{9}{10}$

10) $\frac{65}{12} = 5\frac{5}{12}$ 11) $\frac{31}{10} = 3\frac{1}{10}$ 12) $\frac{17}{2} = 8\frac{1}{2}$

13) $\frac{25}{3} = 8\frac{1}{3}$ 14) $\frac{53}{7} = 7\frac{4}{7}$ 15) $\frac{8}{5} = 1\frac{3}{5}$

16) $\frac{11}{4} = 2\frac{3}{4}$ 17) $\frac{25}{6} = 4\frac{1}{6}$ 18) $\frac{89}{11} = 8\frac{1}{11}$

19) $\frac{79}{10} = 7\frac{9}{10}$ 20) $\frac{42}{11} = 3\frac{9}{11}$ 21) $\frac{22}{3} = 7\frac{1}{3}$

Convert the improper fractions to mixed numbers.

1) $\frac{11}{3} = 3\frac{2}{3}$ 2) $\frac{53}{11} = 4\frac{9}{11}$ 3) $\frac{31}{12} = 2\frac{7}{12}$

4) $\frac{53}{8} = 6\frac{5}{8}$ 5) $\frac{18}{5} = 3\frac{3}{5}$ 6) $\frac{87}{10} = 8\frac{7}{10}$

7) $\frac{91}{11} = 8\frac{3}{11}$ 8) $\frac{47}{10} = 4\frac{7}{10}$ 9) $\frac{23}{4} = 5\frac{3}{4}$

10) $\frac{24}{5} = 4\frac{4}{5}$ 11) $\frac{95}{11} = 8\frac{7}{11}$ 12) $\frac{11}{8} = 1\frac{3}{8}$

13) $\frac{93}{11} = 8\frac{5}{11}$ 14) $\frac{91}{12} = 7\frac{7}{12}$ 15) $\frac{41}{5} = 8\frac{1}{5}$

16) $\frac{13}{8} = 1\frac{5}{8}$ 17) $\frac{35}{4} = 8\frac{3}{4}$ 18) $\frac{17}{6} = 2\frac{5}{6}$

19) $\frac{20}{7} = 2\frac{6}{7}$ 20) $\frac{31}{10} = 3\frac{1}{10}$ 21) $\frac{20}{3} = 6\frac{2}{3}$

Compare the fractions and write the correct symbol (<, = or >) in each box.

1) $\frac{9}{12} > \frac{1}{8}$ 2) $\frac{3}{7} < \frac{5}{6}$ 3) $\frac{2}{10} \;\square\; \frac{9}{11}$

4) $\frac{4}{11} < \frac{7}{10}$ 5) $\frac{1}{3} > \frac{2}{8}$ 6) $\frac{4}{8} = \frac{28}{56}$

7) $\frac{1}{12} < \frac{5}{6}$ 8) $\frac{7}{10} < \frac{8}{11}$ 9) $\frac{7}{9} > \frac{4}{7}$

10) $\frac{4}{6} < \frac{9}{12}$ 11) $\frac{4}{5} > \frac{3}{8}$ 12) $\frac{8}{10} > \frac{2}{9}$

13) $\frac{3}{9} < \frac{7}{8}$ 14) $\frac{6}{7} > \frac{3}{5}$ 15) $\frac{5}{8} > \frac{3}{6}$

16) $\frac{45}{50} = \frac{9}{10}$ 17) $\frac{3}{10} = \frac{9}{30}$ 18) $\frac{5}{7} < \frac{4}{5}$

19) $\frac{5}{10} > \frac{1}{8}$ 20) $\frac{4}{6} < \frac{7}{10}$ 21) $\frac{9}{11} > \frac{2}{12}$

Compare the fractions and write the correct symbol (<, = or >) in each box.

1) $\frac{3}{7} > \frac{4}{10}$ 2) $\frac{7}{9} = \frac{49}{63}$ 3) $\frac{1}{4} < \frac{8}{10}$

4) $\frac{2}{8} < \frac{7}{11}$ 5) $\frac{9}{11} > \frac{4}{5}$ 6) $\frac{7}{12} < \frac{8}{11}$

7) $\frac{1}{3} > \frac{2}{8}$ 8) $\frac{1}{4} < \frac{6}{9}$ 9) $\frac{5}{8} > \frac{1}{6}$

10) $\frac{8}{9} > \frac{4}{7}$ 11) $\frac{5}{12} < \frac{9}{11}$ 12) $\frac{5}{7} > \frac{1}{4}$

13) $\frac{2}{12} < \frac{8}{9}$ 14) $\frac{7}{8} > \frac{1}{7}$ 15) $\frac{1}{6} < \frac{7}{9}$

16) $\frac{5}{6} > \frac{9}{12}$ 17) $\frac{1}{11} < \frac{5}{8}$ 18) $\frac{8}{20} = \frac{2}{5}$

19) $\frac{8}{11} > \frac{4}{8}$ 20) $\frac{5}{10} < \frac{4}{7}$ 21) $\frac{12}{16} = \frac{3}{4}$

Compare the fractions and write the correct symbol (<, = or >) in each box.

1) $\frac{7}{8} > \frac{3}{10}$ 2) $\frac{2}{3} > \frac{3}{9}$ 3) $\frac{9}{12} > \frac{2}{4}$

4) $\frac{8}{11} > \frac{1}{3}$ 5) $\frac{1}{8} < \frac{8}{12}$ 6) $\frac{2}{4} < \frac{7}{8}$

7) $\frac{1}{3} < \frac{6}{12}$ 8) $\frac{1}{10} < \frac{8}{9}$ 9) $\frac{2}{3} < \frac{8}{10}$

10) $\frac{9}{11} > \frac{3}{6}$ 11) $\frac{8}{12} < \frac{4}{5}$ 12) $\frac{6}{9} > \frac{2}{9}$

13) $\frac{6}{9} > \frac{3}{8}$ 14) $\frac{3}{10} < \frac{5}{9}$ 15) $\frac{3}{9} > \frac{1}{10}$

16) $\frac{7}{11} < \frac{8}{12}$ 17) $\frac{1}{6} < \frac{8}{10}$ 18) $\frac{2}{7} > \frac{1}{4}$

19) $\frac{2}{7} < \frac{3}{4}$ 20) $\frac{6}{8} > \frac{2}{11}$ 21) $\frac{4}{9} < \frac{8}{12}$

Compare the fractions and write the correct symbol (<, = or >) in each box.

1) $\frac{6}{7} < \frac{8}{9}$ 2) $\frac{9}{12} > \frac{1}{7}$ 3) $\frac{2}{11} < \frac{3}{10}$

4) $\frac{1}{8} < \frac{4}{5}$ 5) $\frac{4}{10} < \frac{9}{12}$ 6) $\frac{6}{8} > \frac{4}{9}$

7) $\frac{7}{12} < \frac{5}{6}$ 8) $\frac{5}{8} < \frac{9}{10}$ 9) $\frac{2}{7} = \frac{10}{35}$

10) $\frac{4}{10} < \frac{8}{9}$ 11) $\frac{4}{11} < \frac{5}{8}$ 12) $\frac{7}{9} < \frac{9}{11}$

13) $\frac{1}{11} < \frac{5}{8}$ 14) $\frac{1}{2} < \frac{5}{9}$ 15) $\frac{6}{11} < \frac{5}{6}$

16) $\frac{4}{5} > \frac{9}{12}$ 17) $\frac{2}{9} = \frac{8}{36}$ 18) $\frac{4}{7} < \frac{8}{10}$

19) $\frac{5}{6} > \frac{4}{9}$ 20) $\frac{6}{7} > \frac{3}{5}$ 21) $\frac{1}{3} < \frac{3}{7}$

www.claymaze.com

PAGE: 54

Compare the fractions and write the correct symbol (<, = or >) in each box.

1) $\frac{8}{10}$ > $\frac{6}{8}$ 2) $\frac{1}{7}$ < $\frac{5}{11}$ 3) $\frac{5}{8}$ > $\frac{4}{7}$

4) $\frac{2}{11}$ = $\frac{8}{44}$ 5) $\frac{5}{12}$ < $\frac{8}{10}$ 6) $\frac{7}{9}$ > $\frac{4}{11}$

7) $\frac{1}{7}$ < $\frac{7}{8}$ 8) $\frac{3}{10}$ < $\frac{9}{11}$ 9) $\frac{1}{6}$ < $\frac{4}{8}$

10) $\frac{4}{12}$ > $\frac{2}{10}$ 11) $\frac{6}{8}$ > $\frac{1}{12}$ 12) $\frac{1}{7}$ < $\frac{4}{10}$

13) $\frac{1}{10}$ < $\frac{4}{7}$ 14) $\frac{1}{7}$ < $\frac{8}{10}$ 15) $\frac{8}{12}$ > $\frac{5}{11}$

16) $\frac{2}{11}$ < $\frac{8}{12}$ 17) $\frac{8}{9}$ = $\frac{32}{36}$ 18) $\frac{4}{5}$ > $\frac{1}{7}$

19) $\frac{3}{5}$ > $\frac{1}{9}$ 20) $\frac{3}{11}$ = $\frac{6}{22}$ 21) $\frac{7}{8}$ > $\frac{9}{12}$

PAGE: 55

Compare the fractions and write the correct symbol (<, = or >) in each box.

1) $\frac{9}{10}$ > $\frac{8}{11}$ 2) $\frac{5}{9}$ > $\frac{2}{7}$ 3) $\frac{1}{6}$ < $\frac{7}{12}$

4) $\frac{1}{5}$ < $\frac{6}{12}$ 5) $\frac{1}{8}$ < $\frac{6}{10}$ 6) $\frac{1}{11}$ < $\frac{4}{6}$

7) $\frac{8}{10}$ < $\frac{5}{6}$ 8) $\frac{4}{5}$ > $\frac{7}{12}$ 9) $\frac{2}{8}$ < $\frac{5}{11}$

10) $\frac{4}{8}$ > $\frac{3}{11}$ 11) $\frac{5}{10}$ > $\frac{1}{4}$ 12) $\frac{3}{5}$ = $\frac{9}{15}$

13) $\frac{8}{12}$ < $\frac{5}{7}$ 14) $\frac{3}{8}$ < $\frac{9}{12}$ 15) $\frac{35}{40}$ = $\frac{7}{8}$

16) $\frac{7}{10}$ < $\frac{9}{11}$ 17) $\frac{1}{7}$ < $\frac{4}{5}$ 18) $\frac{3}{11}$ < $\frac{8}{10}$

19) $\frac{3}{12}$ < $\frac{8}{9}$ 20) $\frac{2}{22}$ = $\frac{1}{11}$ 21) $\frac{1}{8}$ < $\frac{6}{7}$

PAGE: 56

Compare the fractions and write the correct symbol (<, = or >) in each box.

1) $\frac{2}{7}$ > $\frac{3}{12}$ 2) $\frac{2}{11}$ < $\frac{6}{7}$ 3) $\frac{4}{7}$ > $\frac{3}{10}$

4) $\frac{1}{4}$ < $\frac{4}{5}$ 5) $\frac{7}{8}$ > $\frac{1}{11}$ 6) $\frac{6}{11}$ > $\frac{1}{4}$

7) $\frac{1}{6}$ < $\frac{5}{9}$ 8) $\frac{6}{12}$ > $\frac{3}{8}$ 9) $\frac{9}{10}$ > $\frac{3}{12}$

10) $\frac{2}{4}$ < $\frac{9}{10}$ 11) $\frac{49}{63}$ = $\frac{7}{9}$ 12) $\frac{7}{9}$ > $\frac{1}{4}$

13) $\frac{3}{10}$ = $\frac{15}{50}$ 14) $\frac{1}{11}$ < $\frac{7}{12}$ 15) $\frac{7}{12}$ > $\frac{6}{11}$

16) $\frac{4}{6}$ > $\frac{5}{8}$ 17) $\frac{3}{8}$ < $\frac{9}{11}$ 18) $\frac{7}{11}$ < $\frac{9}{10}$

19) $\frac{2}{10}$ < $\frac{4}{9}$ 20) $\frac{3}{12}$ > $\frac{1}{5}$ 21) $\frac{1}{8}$ < $\frac{9}{12}$

PAGE: 57

Compare the fractions and write the correct symbol (<, = or >) in each box.

1) $\frac{1}{11}$ < $\frac{2}{10}$ 2) $\frac{4}{10}$ < $\frac{3}{5}$ 3) $\frac{2}{11}$ < $\frac{1}{3}$

4) $\frac{8}{9}$ > $\frac{7}{11}$ 5) $\frac{5}{12}$ > $\frac{3}{9}$ 6) $\frac{4}{6}$ > $\frac{5}{8}$

7) $\frac{2}{6}$ < $\frac{9}{12}$ 8) $\frac{5}{10}$ < $\frac{6}{7}$ 9) $\frac{3}{9}$ > $\frac{2}{10}$

10) $\frac{2}{12}$ < $\frac{5}{9}$ 11) $\frac{1}{6}$ < $\frac{6}{12}$ 12) $\frac{5}{11}$ < $\frac{2}{3}$

13) $\frac{4}{6}$ < $\frac{8}{10}$ 14) $\frac{8}{9}$ = $\frac{24}{27}$ 15) $\frac{9}{12}$ = $\frac{6}{8}$

16) $\frac{6}{9}$ = $\frac{2}{3}$ 17) $\frac{3}{7}$ > $\frac{1}{6}$ 18) $\frac{5}{11}$ = $\frac{35}{77}$

19) $\frac{6}{11}$ < $\frac{7}{10}$ 20) $\frac{1}{12}$ < $\frac{3}{8}$ 21) $\frac{3}{7}$ > $\frac{2}{9}$

PAGE: 58

Compare the fractions and write the correct symbol (<, = or >) in each box.

1) $\frac{3}{12}$ > $\frac{1}{9}$ 2) $\frac{5}{8}$ < $\frac{9}{11}$ 3) $\frac{16}{48}$ = $\frac{4}{12}$

4) $\frac{3}{10}$ < $\frac{5}{6}$ 5) $\frac{1}{5}$ < $\frac{5}{7}$ 6) $\frac{7}{10}$ > $\frac{1}{8}$

7) $\frac{3}{11}$ < $\frac{9}{10}$ 8) $\frac{4}{10}$ < $\frac{8}{9}$ 9) $\frac{15}{60}$ = $\frac{3}{12}$

10) $\frac{4}{8}$ > $\frac{1}{4}$ 11) $\frac{2}{12}$ < $\frac{3}{8}$ 12) $\frac{3}{6}$ < $\frac{9}{11}$

13) $\frac{5}{6}$ = $\frac{35}{42}$ 14) $\frac{4}{16}$ = $\frac{1}{4}$ 15) $\frac{8}{12}$ > $\frac{1}{7}$

16) $\frac{1}{9}$ < $\frac{5}{7}$ 17) $\frac{5}{11}$ < $\frac{8}{9}$ 18) $\frac{7}{10}$ > $\frac{4}{8}$

19) $\frac{2}{5}$ < $\frac{9}{12}$ 20) $\frac{18}{21}$ = $\frac{6}{7}$ 21) $\frac{1}{9}$ < $\frac{9}{10}$

PAGE: 59

Compare the fractions and write the correct symbol (<, = or >) in each box.

1) $\frac{7}{8}$ > $\frac{8}{12}$ 2) $\frac{2}{10}$ < $\frac{3}{6}$ 3) $\frac{5}{6}$ > $\frac{9}{12}$

4) $\frac{8}{10}$ < $\frac{6}{7}$ 5) $\frac{5}{8}$ < $\frac{3}{4}$ 6) $\frac{7}{10}$ < $\frac{8}{11}$

7) $\frac{2}{7}$ < $\frac{9}{11}$ 8) $\frac{5}{10}$ < $\frac{4}{9}$ 9) $\frac{1}{9}$ < $\frac{7}{10}$

10) $\frac{4}{10}$ < $\frac{6}{8}$ 11) $\frac{1}{2}$ > $\frac{5}{11}$ 12) $\frac{4}{8}$ = $\frac{28}{56}$

13) $\frac{5}{11}$ < $\frac{8}{10}$ 14) $\frac{8}{9}$ > $\frac{6}{12}$ 15) $\frac{4}{11}$ > $\frac{1}{10}$

16) $\frac{12}{14}$ = $\frac{6}{7}$ 17) $\frac{6}{12}$ > $\frac{2}{8}$ 18) $\frac{8}{10}$ > $\frac{1}{2}$

19) $\frac{5}{9}$ < $\frac{9}{12}$ 20) $\frac{8}{11}$ = $\frac{32}{44}$ 21) $\frac{2}{4}$ > $\frac{1}{8}$

www.claymaze.com

Compare the fractions and write the correct symbol (<, = or >) in each box.

1) $\frac{2}{5}$ = $\frac{4}{10}$ 2) $\frac{3}{6}$ > $\frac{1}{8}$ 3) $\frac{4}{12}$ < $\frac{2}{4}$

4) $\frac{1}{2}$ < $\frac{5}{9}$ 5) $\frac{9}{11}$ > $\frac{2}{10}$ 6) $\frac{5}{9}$ < $\frac{3}{5}$

7) $\frac{4}{8}$ < $\frac{6}{7}$ 8) $\frac{3}{12}$ < $\frac{8}{9}$ 9) $\frac{7}{10}$ < $\frac{9}{11}$

10) $\frac{1}{3}$ > $\frac{2}{10}$ 11) $\frac{7}{10}$ < $\frac{8}{11}$ 12) $\frac{5}{6}$ > $\frac{2}{8}$

13) $\frac{7}{9}$ > $\frac{6}{11}$ 14) $\frac{7}{11}$ < $\frac{9}{12}$ 15) $\frac{56}{70}$ = $\frac{8}{10}$

16) $\frac{7}{11}$ > $\frac{4}{7}$ 17) $\frac{2}{8}$ < $\frac{7}{10}$ 18) $\frac{7}{12}$ > $\frac{1}{2}$

19) $\frac{2}{8}$ < $\frac{9}{10}$ 20) $\frac{8}{9}$ > $\frac{5}{12}$ 21) $\frac{1}{3}$ < $\frac{9}{11}$

Add the fractions and simplify.

1) $\frac{1}{10} + \frac{5}{8} = \frac{29}{40}$

2) $\frac{4}{7} + \frac{8}{11} = 1\frac{23}{77}$

3) $\frac{3}{8} + \frac{3}{7} = \frac{45}{56}$

4) $\frac{9}{12} + \frac{5}{6} = 1\frac{7}{12}$

Subtract the fractions and simplify.

5) $\frac{6}{8} - \frac{6}{11} = \frac{9}{44}$

6) $\frac{9}{12} - \frac{4}{7} = \frac{5}{28}$

7) $\frac{7}{8} - \frac{3}{5} = \frac{11}{40}$

8) $\frac{7}{9} - \frac{5}{7} = \frac{4}{63}$

Add the fractions and simplify.

1) $\frac{9}{11} + \frac{7}{8} = 1\frac{61}{88}$

2) $\frac{2}{9} + \frac{1}{5} = \frac{19}{45}$

3) $\frac{4}{12} + \frac{5}{7} = 1\frac{1}{21}$

4) $\frac{7}{11} + \frac{9}{12} = 1\frac{17}{44}$

Subtract the fractions and simplify.

5) $\frac{8}{10} - \frac{5}{11} = \frac{19}{55}$

6) $\frac{9}{12} - \frac{1}{10} = \frac{13}{20}$

7) $\frac{3}{4} - \frac{5}{8} = \frac{1}{8}$

8) $\frac{6}{9} - \frac{4}{10} = \frac{4}{15}$

Add the fractions and simplify.

1) $\frac{1}{4} + \frac{9}{11} = 1\frac{3}{44}$

2) $\frac{2}{5} + \frac{9}{10} = 1\frac{3}{10}$

3) $\frac{5}{7} + \frac{1}{8} = \frac{47}{56}$

4) $\frac{2}{12} + \frac{8}{11} = \frac{59}{66}$

Subtract the fractions and simplify.

5) $\frac{9}{10} - \frac{4}{7} = \frac{23}{70}$

6) $\frac{8}{9} - \frac{5}{11} = \frac{43}{99}$

7) $\frac{8}{12} - \frac{4}{9} = \frac{2}{9}$

8) $\frac{2}{5} - \frac{1}{11} = \frac{17}{55}$

Add the fractions and simplify.

1) $\frac{2}{10} + \frac{6}{8} = \frac{19}{20}$

2) $\frac{1}{2} + \frac{8}{10} = 1\frac{3}{10}$

3) $\frac{5}{9} + \frac{5}{6} = 1\frac{7}{18}$

4) $\frac{5}{8} + \frac{3}{10} = \frac{37}{40}$

Subtract the fractions and simplify.

5) $\frac{9}{10} - \frac{9}{11} = \frac{9}{110}$

6) $\frac{6}{8} - \frac{1}{3} = \frac{5}{12}$

7) $\frac{1}{6} - \frac{1}{8} = \frac{1}{24}$

8) $\frac{6}{7} - \frac{3}{11} = \frac{45}{77}$

Add the fractions and simplify.

1) $\frac{6}{11} + \frac{8}{10} = 1\frac{19}{55}$

2) $\frac{5}{9} + \frac{3}{8} = \frac{67}{72}$

3) $\frac{7}{12} + \frac{3}{4} = 1\frac{1}{3}$

4) $\frac{9}{11} + \frac{5}{9} = 1\frac{37}{99}$

Subtract the fractions and simplify.

5) $\frac{8}{9} - \frac{3}{10} = \frac{53}{90}$

6) $\frac{5}{7} - \frac{1}{12} = \frac{53}{84}$

7) $\frac{7}{8} - \frac{8}{11} = \frac{13}{88}$

8) $\frac{4}{5} - \frac{5}{12} = \frac{23}{60}$

www.claymaze.com

Add the fractions and simplify.

1) $\frac{6}{7} + \frac{2}{12} = 1\frac{1}{42}$

2) $\frac{3}{8} + \frac{3}{10} = \frac{27}{40}$

3) $\frac{2}{9} + \frac{3}{12} = \frac{17}{36}$

4) $\frac{9}{11} + \frac{5}{7} = 1\frac{41}{77}$

Subtract the fractions and simplify.

5) $\frac{5}{6} - \frac{2}{5} = \frac{13}{30}$

6) $\frac{9}{10} - \frac{7}{11} = \frac{29}{110}$

7) $\frac{7}{8} - \frac{5}{9} = \frac{23}{72}$

8) $\frac{8}{11} - \frac{1}{7} = \frac{45}{77}$

Add the fractions and simplify.

1) $\frac{6}{8} + \frac{3}{10} = 1\frac{1}{20}$

2) $\frac{4}{12} + \frac{5}{8} = \frac{23}{24}$

3) $\frac{5}{11} + \frac{6}{7} = 1\frac{24}{77}$

4) $\frac{5}{6} + \frac{2}{5} = 1\frac{7}{30}$

Subtract the fractions and simplify.

5) $\frac{9}{12} - \frac{5}{10} = \frac{1}{4}$

6) $\frac{7}{8} - \frac{9}{12} = \frac{1}{8}$

7) $\frac{9}{11} - \frac{8}{10} = \frac{1}{55}$

8) $\frac{8}{9} - \frac{3}{8} = \frac{37}{72}$

Add the fractions and simplify.

1) $\frac{7}{12} + \frac{3}{8} = \frac{23}{24}$

2) $\frac{2}{7} + \frac{7}{12} = \frac{73}{84}$

3) $\frac{5}{12} + \frac{7}{9} = 1\frac{7}{36}$

4) $\frac{8}{9} + \frac{1}{3} = 1\frac{2}{9}$

Subtract the fractions and simplify.

5) $\frac{9}{10} - \frac{1}{2} = \frac{2}{5}$

6) $\frac{3}{11} - \frac{1}{4} = \frac{1}{44}$

7) $\frac{9}{12} - \frac{3}{9} = \frac{5}{12}$

8) $\frac{6}{7} - \frac{6}{10} = \frac{9}{35}$

Add the fractions and simplify.

1) $\frac{6}{7} + \frac{9}{10} = 1\frac{53}{70}$

2) $\frac{8}{11} + \frac{2}{8} = \frac{43}{44}$

3) $\frac{3}{10} + \frac{5}{7} = 1\frac{1}{70}$

4) $\frac{4}{11} + \frac{7}{9} = 1\frac{14}{99}$

Subtract the fractions and simplify.

5) $\frac{2}{3} - \frac{1}{6} = \frac{1}{2}$

6) $\frac{3}{8} - \frac{2}{10} = \frac{7}{40}$

7) $\frac{9}{12} - \frac{2}{11} = \frac{25}{44}$

8) $\frac{8}{9} - \frac{8}{10} = \frac{4}{45}$

Add the fractions and simplify.

1) $\frac{4}{9} + \frac{3}{5} = 1\frac{2}{45}$

2) $\frac{1}{5} + \frac{7}{10} = \frac{9}{10}$

3) $\frac{1}{12} + \frac{2}{5} = \frac{29}{60}$

4) $\frac{6}{9} + \frac{1}{8} = \frac{19}{24}$

Subtract the fractions and simplify.

5) $\frac{3}{4} - \frac{4}{10} = \frac{7}{20}$

6) $\frac{2}{3} - \frac{5}{9} = \frac{1}{9}$

7) $\frac{9}{11} - \frac{4}{5} = \frac{1}{55}$

8) $\frac{9}{10} - \frac{5}{9} = \frac{31}{90}$

Add the fractions and simplify.

1) $\frac{9}{10} + \frac{2}{3} = 1\frac{17}{30}$

2) $\frac{7}{12} + \frac{3}{7} = 1\frac{1}{84}$

3) $\frac{4}{7} + \frac{1}{6} = \frac{31}{42}$

4) $\frac{4}{10} + \frac{7}{8} = 1\frac{11}{40}$

Subtract the fractions and simplify.

5) $\frac{7}{9} - \frac{3}{4} = \frac{1}{36}$

6) $\frac{9}{11} - \frac{4}{7} = \frac{19}{77}$

7) $\frac{1}{3} - \frac{3}{11} = \frac{2}{33}$

8) $\frac{3}{5} - \frac{2}{12} = \frac{13}{30}$

www.claymaze.com

Multiply the fractions and simplify.

1) $\dfrac{4}{11} \times \dfrac{2}{5} = \dfrac{8}{55}$

2) $\dfrac{6}{8} \times \dfrac{4}{9} = \dfrac{1}{3}$

3) $\dfrac{2}{4} \times \dfrac{4}{11} = \dfrac{2}{11}$

4) $\dfrac{5}{9} \times \dfrac{5}{6} = \dfrac{25}{54}$

Divide the fractions and simplify.

5) $\dfrac{6}{11} \div \dfrac{6}{12} = 1\dfrac{1}{11}$

6) $\dfrac{5}{6} \div \dfrac{1}{5} = 4\dfrac{1}{6}$

7) $\dfrac{7}{10} \div \dfrac{3}{12} = 2\dfrac{4}{5}$

8) $\dfrac{5}{12} \div \dfrac{4}{10} = 1\dfrac{1}{24}$

Multiply the fractions and simplify.

1) $\dfrac{2}{7} \times \dfrac{7}{9} = \dfrac{2}{9}$

2) $\dfrac{7}{9} \times \dfrac{2}{4} = \dfrac{7}{18}$

3) $\dfrac{2}{11} \times \dfrac{5}{7} = \dfrac{10}{77}$

4) $\dfrac{4}{8} \times \dfrac{2}{10} = \dfrac{1}{10}$

Divide the fractions and simplify.

5) $\dfrac{2}{4} \div \dfrac{4}{11} = 1\dfrac{3}{8}$

6) $\dfrac{5}{6} \div \dfrac{3}{4} = 1\dfrac{1}{9}$

7) $\dfrac{4}{10} \div \dfrac{3}{8} = 1\dfrac{1}{15}$

8) $\dfrac{7}{10} \div \dfrac{2}{5} = 1\dfrac{3}{4}$

Multiply the fractions and simplify.

1) $\dfrac{1}{9} \times \dfrac{2}{3} = \dfrac{2}{27}$

2) $\dfrac{6}{8} \times \dfrac{5}{6} = \dfrac{5}{8}$

3) $\dfrac{8}{11} \times \dfrac{2}{10} = \dfrac{8}{55}$

4) $\dfrac{1}{6} \times \dfrac{6}{9} = \dfrac{1}{9}$

Divide the fractions and simplify.

5) $\dfrac{8}{9} \div \dfrac{9}{11} = 1\dfrac{7}{81}$

6) $\dfrac{3}{4} \div \dfrac{3}{6} = 1\dfrac{1}{2}$

7) $\dfrac{8}{9} \div \dfrac{7}{8} = 1\dfrac{1}{63}$

8) $\dfrac{6}{8} \div \dfrac{5}{10} = 1\dfrac{1}{2}$

Multiply the fractions and simplify.

1) $\dfrac{1}{7} \times \dfrac{7}{9} = \dfrac{1}{9}$

2) $\dfrac{5}{6} \times \dfrac{7}{10} = \dfrac{7}{12}$

3) $\dfrac{9}{10} \times \dfrac{1}{7} = \dfrac{9}{70}$

4) $\dfrac{6}{12} \times \dfrac{8}{10} = \dfrac{2}{5}$

Divide the fractions and simplify.

5) $\dfrac{4}{6} \div \dfrac{4}{7} = 1\dfrac{1}{6}$

6) $\dfrac{6}{10} \div \dfrac{5}{9} = 1\dfrac{2}{25}$

7) $\dfrac{5}{8} \div \dfrac{6}{12} = 1\dfrac{1}{4}$

8) $\dfrac{7}{12} \div \dfrac{2}{7} = 2\dfrac{1}{24}$

Multiply the fractions and simplify.

1) $\dfrac{6}{12} \times \dfrac{8}{10} = \dfrac{2}{5}$

2) $\dfrac{3}{6} \times \dfrac{3}{9} = \dfrac{1}{6}$

3) $\dfrac{7}{12} \times \dfrac{7}{10} = \dfrac{49}{120}$

4) $\dfrac{1}{11} \times \dfrac{3}{8} = \dfrac{3}{88}$

Divide the fractions and simplify.

5) $\dfrac{6}{7} \div \dfrac{3}{12} = 3\dfrac{3}{7}$

6) $\dfrac{6}{11} \div \dfrac{2}{10} = 2\dfrac{8}{11}$

7) $\dfrac{9}{12} \div \dfrac{2}{3} = 1\dfrac{1}{8}$

8) $\dfrac{2}{3} \div \dfrac{7}{11} = 1\dfrac{1}{21}$

Multiply the fractions and simplify.

1) $\dfrac{1}{6} \times \dfrac{8}{9} = \dfrac{4}{27}$

2) $\dfrac{4}{12} \times \dfrac{2}{5} = \dfrac{2}{15}$

3) $\dfrac{8}{11} \times \dfrac{7}{12} = \dfrac{14}{33}$

4) $\dfrac{1}{8} \times \dfrac{5}{11} = \dfrac{5}{88}$

Divide the fractions and simplify.

5) $\dfrac{7}{12} \div \dfrac{1}{3} = 1\dfrac{3}{4}$

6) $\dfrac{5}{7} \div \dfrac{7}{10} = 1\dfrac{1}{49}$

7) $\dfrac{7}{10} \div \dfrac{4}{9} = 1\dfrac{23}{40}$

8) $\dfrac{7}{12} \div \dfrac{1}{7} = 4\dfrac{1}{12}$

www.claymaze.com

PAGE: 80

Multiply the fractions and simplify.

1) $\dfrac{9}{11} \times \dfrac{3}{6} = \dfrac{9}{22}$

2) $\dfrac{1}{10} \times \dfrac{1}{4} = \dfrac{1}{40}$

3) $\dfrac{6}{7} \times \dfrac{8}{9} = \dfrac{16}{21}$

4) $\dfrac{7}{11} \times \dfrac{2}{12} = \dfrac{7}{66}$

Divide the fractions and simplify.

5) $\dfrac{7}{10} \div \dfrac{1}{5} = 3\dfrac{1}{2}$

6) $\dfrac{7}{9} \div \dfrac{3}{8} = 2\dfrac{2}{27}$

7) $\dfrac{2}{5} \div \dfrac{1}{11} = 4\dfrac{2}{5}$

8) $\dfrac{8}{11} \div \dfrac{4}{12} = 2\dfrac{2}{11}$

PAGE: 81

Multiply the fractions and simplify.

1) $\dfrac{5}{10} \times \dfrac{7}{9} = \dfrac{7}{18}$

2) $\dfrac{6}{7} \times \dfrac{6}{12} = \dfrac{3}{7}$

3) $\dfrac{2}{3} \times \dfrac{8}{11} = \dfrac{16}{33}$

4) $\dfrac{1}{6} \times \dfrac{3}{10} = \dfrac{1}{20}$

Divide the fractions and simplify.

5) $\dfrac{5}{7} \div \dfrac{3}{11} = 2\dfrac{13}{21}$

6) $\dfrac{9}{11} \div \dfrac{7}{12} = 1\dfrac{31}{77}$

7) $\dfrac{6}{12} \div \dfrac{4}{11} = 1\dfrac{3}{8}$

8) $\dfrac{2}{7} \div \dfrac{1}{8} = 2\dfrac{2}{7}$

PAGE: 82

Multiply the fractions and simplify.

1) $\dfrac{1}{5} \times \dfrac{7}{11} = \dfrac{7}{55}$

2) $\dfrac{9}{11} \times \dfrac{5}{8} = \dfrac{45}{88}$

3) $\dfrac{7}{8} \times \dfrac{5}{9} = \dfrac{35}{72}$

4) $\dfrac{9}{10} \times \dfrac{4}{7} = \dfrac{18}{35}$

Divide the fractions and simplify.

5) $\dfrac{7}{11} \div \dfrac{3}{12} = 2\dfrac{6}{11}$

6) $\dfrac{9}{10} \div \dfrac{1}{5} = 4\dfrac{1}{2}$

7) $\dfrac{4}{8} \div \dfrac{3}{7} = 1\dfrac{1}{6}$

8) $\dfrac{8}{11} \div \dfrac{4}{6} = 1\dfrac{1}{11}$

PAGE: 83

Multiply the fractions and simplify.

1) $\dfrac{8}{11} \times \dfrac{3}{6} = \dfrac{4}{11}$

2) $\dfrac{6}{9} \times \dfrac{1}{11} = \dfrac{2}{33}$

3) $\dfrac{7}{11} \times \dfrac{2}{7} = \dfrac{2}{11}$

4) $\dfrac{4}{7} \times \dfrac{8}{10} = \dfrac{16}{35}$

Divide the fractions and simplify.

5) $\dfrac{6}{10} \div \dfrac{4}{7} = 1\dfrac{1}{20}$

6) $\dfrac{7}{9} \div \dfrac{1}{11} = 8\dfrac{5}{9}$

7) $\dfrac{6}{7} \div \dfrac{6}{9} = 1\dfrac{2}{7}$

8) $\dfrac{6}{10} \div \dfrac{1}{3} = 1\dfrac{4}{5}$

PAGE: 84

Multiply the fractions and simplify.

1) $\dfrac{4}{5} \times \dfrac{3}{11} = \dfrac{12}{55}$

2) $\dfrac{6}{12} \times \dfrac{1}{4} = \dfrac{1}{8}$

3) $\dfrac{5}{10} \times \dfrac{2}{3} = \dfrac{1}{3}$

4) $\dfrac{2}{3} \times \dfrac{1}{6} = \dfrac{1}{9}$

Divide the fractions and simplify.

5) $\dfrac{3}{5} \div \dfrac{5}{9} = 1\dfrac{2}{25}$

6) $\dfrac{7}{8} \div \dfrac{3}{4} = 1\dfrac{1}{6}$

7) $\dfrac{8}{11} \div \dfrac{8}{12} = 1\dfrac{1}{11}$

8) $\dfrac{4}{6} \div \dfrac{4}{7} = 1\dfrac{1}{6}$

PAGE: 86

Convert the fractions to decimals.

1) $\dfrac{6}{10} = .6$

2) $\dfrac{265}{1000} = .265$

3) $\dfrac{4}{100} = .04$

4) $\dfrac{50}{100} = .5$

5) $\dfrac{2}{100} = .02$

6) $\dfrac{3}{10} = .3$

7) $\dfrac{8}{1000} = .008$

8) $\dfrac{198}{1000} = .198$

9) $\dfrac{28}{100} = .28$

10) $\dfrac{2}{10} = .2$

11) $\dfrac{46}{1000} = .046$

12) $\dfrac{122}{1000} = .122$

Convert the decimals to fractions. Write as 10ths, 100ths or 1000ths.

13) $.029 = \dfrac{29}{1000}$

14) $.9 = \dfrac{9}{10}$

15) $.01 = \dfrac{1}{100}$

16) $.24 = \dfrac{24}{100}$

17) $.44 = \dfrac{44}{100}$

18) $.04 = \dfrac{4}{100}$

19) $.69 = \dfrac{69}{100}$

20) $.536 = \dfrac{536}{1000}$

21) $.631 = \dfrac{631}{1000}$

22) $.4 = \dfrac{4}{10}$

23) $.54 = \dfrac{54}{100}$

24) $.47 = \dfrac{47}{100}$

www.claymaze.com

Convert the fractions to decimals.

1) $\frac{76}{1000}$ = .076 2) $\frac{846}{1000}$ = .846 3) $\frac{45}{100}$ = .45

4) $\frac{5}{10}$ = .5 5) $\frac{40}{100}$ = .4 6) $\frac{41}{1000}$ = .041

7) $\frac{1}{10}$ = .1 8) $\frac{12}{100}$ = .12 9) $\frac{89}{100}$ = .89

10) $\frac{517}{1000}$ = .517 11) $\frac{3}{100}$ = .03 12) $\frac{38}{100}$ = .38

Convert the decimals to fractions. Write as 10ths, 100ths or 1000ths.

13) .16 = $\frac{16}{100}$ 14) .09 = $\frac{9}{100}$ 15) .2 = $\frac{2}{10}$

16) .094 = $\frac{94}{1000}$ 17) .7 = $\frac{7}{10}$ 18) .537 = $\frac{537}{1000}$

19) .19 = $\frac{19}{100}$ 20) .6 = $\frac{6}{10}$ 21) .017 = $\frac{17}{1000}$

22) .85 = $\frac{85}{100}$ 23) .1 = $\frac{1}{10}$ 24) .04 = $\frac{4}{100}$

Convert the fractions to decimals.

1) $\frac{7}{10}$ = .7 2) $\frac{1}{10}$ = .1 3) $\frac{5}{100}$ = .05

4) $\frac{2}{100}$ = .02 5) $\frac{8}{100}$ = .08 6) $\frac{1}{100}$ = .01

7) $\frac{3}{10}$ = .3 8) $\frac{5}{10}$ = .5 9) $\frac{71}{1000}$ = .071

10) $\frac{9}{10}$ = .9 11) $\frac{6}{10}$ = .6 12) $\frac{4}{100}$ = .04

Convert the decimals to fractions. Write as 10ths, 100ths or 1000ths.

13) .5 = $\frac{5}{10}$ 14) .672 = $\frac{672}{1000}$ 15) .007 = $\frac{7}{1000}$

16) .246 = $\frac{246}{1000}$ 17) .7 = $\frac{7}{10}$ 18) .017 = $\frac{17}{1000}$

19) .55 = $\frac{55}{100}$ 20) .004 = $\frac{4}{1000}$ 21) .2 = $\frac{2}{10}$

22) .079 = $\frac{79}{1000}$ 23) .024 = $\frac{24}{1000}$ 24) .6 = $\frac{6}{10}$

Convert the fractions to decimals.

1) $\frac{8}{100}$ = .08 2) $\frac{67}{1000}$ = .067 3) $\frac{65}{100}$ = .65

4) $\frac{85}{100}$ = .85 5) $\frac{6}{10}$ = .6 6) $\frac{889}{1000}$ = .889

7) $\frac{74}{100}$ = .74 8) $\frac{3}{10}$ = .3 9) $\frac{84}{1000}$ = .084

10) $\frac{37}{100}$ = .37 11) $\frac{7}{100}$ = .07 12) $\frac{764}{1000}$ = .764

Convert the decimals to fractions. Write as 10ths, 100ths or 1000ths.

13) .7 = $\frac{7}{10}$ 14) .2 = $\frac{2}{10}$ 15) .071 = $\frac{71}{1000}$

16) .65 = $\frac{65}{100}$ 17) .236 = $\frac{236}{1000}$ 18) .095 = $\frac{95}{1000}$

19) .792 = $\frac{792}{1000}$ 20) .518 = $\frac{518}{1000}$ 21) .5 = $\frac{5}{10}$

22) .198 = $\frac{198}{1000}$ 23) .8 = $\frac{8}{10}$ 24) .001 = $\frac{1}{1000}$

Convert the fractions to decimals.

1) $\frac{2}{10}$ = .2 2) $\frac{49}{100}$ = .49 3) $\frac{82}{1000}$ = .082

4) $\frac{82}{100}$ = .82 5) $\frac{98}{1000}$ = .098 6) $\frac{40}{1000}$ = .04

7) $\frac{58}{100}$ = .58 8) $\frac{26}{100}$ = .26 9) $\frac{83}{100}$ = .83

10) $\frac{93}{100}$ = .93 11) $\frac{631}{1000}$ = .631 12) $\frac{84}{100}$ = .84

Convert the decimals to fractions. Write as 10ths, 100ths or 1000ths.

13) .632 = $\frac{632}{1000}$ 14) .1 = $\frac{1}{10}$ 15) .07 = $\frac{7}{100}$

16) .3 = $\frac{3}{10}$ 17) .54 = $\frac{54}{100}$ 18) .99 = $\frac{99}{100}$

19) .4 = $\frac{4}{10}$ 20) .011 = $\frac{11}{1000}$ 21) .61 = $\frac{61}{100}$

22) .086 = $\frac{86}{1000}$ 23) .001 = $\frac{1}{1000}$ 24) .2 = $\frac{2}{10}$

Convert the fractions to decimals.

1) $\frac{13}{100}$ = .13 2) $\frac{41}{100}$ = .41 3) $\frac{54}{1000}$ = .054

4) $\frac{9}{100}$ = .09 5) $\frac{3}{10}$ = .3 6) $\frac{47}{100}$ = .47

7) $\frac{6}{10}$ = .6 8) $\frac{533}{1000}$ = .533 9) $\frac{98}{100}$ = .98

10) $\frac{5}{10}$ = .5 11) $\frac{51}{100}$ = .51 12) $\frac{10}{1000}$ = .01

Convert the decimals to fractions. Write as 10ths, 100ths or 1000ths.

13) .05 = $\frac{5}{100}$ 14) .966 = $\frac{966}{1000}$ 15) .3 = $\frac{3}{10}$

16) .01 = $\frac{1}{100}$ 17) .48 = $\frac{48}{100}$ 18) .6 = $\frac{6}{10}$

19) .337 = $\frac{337}{1000}$ 20) .77 = $\frac{77}{100}$ 21) .287 = $\frac{287}{1000}$

22) .7 = $\frac{7}{10}$ 23) .64 = $\frac{64}{100}$ 24) .58 = $\frac{58}{100}$

Convert the fractions to decimals.

1) $\frac{82}{1000}$ = .082 2) $\frac{704}{1000}$ = .704 3) $\frac{1}{10}$ = .1

4) $\frac{8}{100}$ = .08 5) $\frac{80}{100}$ = .8 6) $\frac{251}{1000}$ = .251

7) $\frac{714}{1000}$ = .714 8) $\frac{8}{10}$ = .8 9) $\frac{2}{10}$ = .2

10) $\frac{4}{10}$ = .4 11) $\frac{56}{1000}$ = .056 12) $\frac{74}{100}$ = .74

Convert the decimals to fractions. Write as 10ths, 100ths or 1000ths.

13) .492 = $\frac{492}{1000}$ 14) .5 = $\frac{5}{10}$ 15) .03 = $\frac{3}{100}$

16) .4 = $\frac{4}{10}$ 17) .9 = $\frac{9}{10}$ 18) .11 = $\frac{11}{100}$

19) .31 = $\frac{31}{100}$ 20) .701 = $\frac{701}{1000}$ 21) .659 = $\frac{659}{1000}$

22) .2 = $\frac{2}{10}$ 23) .7 = $\frac{7}{10}$ 24) .68 = $\frac{68}{100}$

www.claymaze.com

Convert the fractions to decimals.

1) $\frac{2}{100}$ = .02   2) $\frac{870}{1000}$ = .87   3) $\frac{2}{10}$ = .2

4) $\frac{4}{1000}$ = .004   5) $\frac{8}{10}$ = .8   6) $\frac{6}{100}$ = .06

7) $\frac{7}{10}$ = .7   8) $\frac{43}{1000}$ = .043   9) $\frac{531}{1000}$ = .531

10) $\frac{300}{1000}$ = .3   11) $\frac{1}{10}$ = .1   12) $\frac{4}{10}$ = .4

Convert the decimals to fractions. Write as 10ths, 100ths or 1000ths.

13) .23 = $\frac{23}{100}$ 14) .6 = $\frac{6}{10}$ 15) .7 = $\frac{7}{10}$

16) .077 = $\frac{77}{1000}$ 17) .3 = $\frac{3}{10}$ 18) .083 = $\frac{83}{1000}$

19) .63 = $\frac{63}{100}$ 20) .627 = $\frac{627}{1000}$ 21) .9 = $\frac{9}{10}$

22) .5 = $\frac{5}{10}$ 23) .8 = $\frac{8}{10}$ 24) .67 = $\frac{67}{100}$

Convert the fractions to decimals.

1) $\frac{9}{10}$ = .9   2) $\frac{3}{1000}$ = .003   3) $\frac{8}{10}$ = .8

4) $\frac{6}{10}$ = .6   5) $\frac{2}{1000}$ = .002   6) $\frac{5}{10}$ = .5

7) $\frac{198}{1000}$ = .198   8) $\frac{366}{1000}$ = .366   9) $\frac{81}{1000}$ = .081

10) $\frac{4}{10}$ = .4   11) $\frac{81}{100}$ = .81   12) $\frac{82}{1000}$ = .082

Convert the decimals to fractions. Write as 10ths, 100ths or 1000ths.

13) .389 = $\frac{389}{1000}$ 14) .7 = $\frac{7}{10}$ 15) .142 = $\frac{142}{1000}$

16) .46 = $\frac{46}{100}$ 17) .052 = $\frac{52}{1000}$ 18) .076 = $\frac{76}{1000}$

19) .273 = $\frac{273}{1000}$ 20) .8 = $\frac{8}{10}$ 21) .9 = $\frac{9}{10}$

22) .2 = $\frac{2}{10}$ 23) .24 = $\frac{24}{100}$ 24) .58 = $\frac{58}{100}$

Convert the fractions to decimals.

1) $\frac{4}{10}$ = .4   2) $\frac{59}{100}$ = .59   3) $\frac{7}{10}$ = .7

4) $\frac{45}{100}$ = .45   5) $\frac{12}{100}$ = .12   6) $\frac{1}{10}$ = .1

7) $\frac{5}{100}$ = .05   8) $\frac{3}{10}$ = .3   9) $\frac{19}{100}$ = .19

10) $\frac{7}{100}$ = .07   11) $\frac{77}{100}$ = .77   12) $\frac{266}{1000}$ = .266

Convert the decimals to fractions. Write as 10ths, 100ths or 1000ths.

13) .698 = $\frac{698}{1000}$ 14) .3 = $\frac{3}{10}$ 15) .006 = $\frac{6}{1000}$

16) .9 = $\frac{9}{10}$ 17) .493 = $\frac{493}{1000}$ 18) .153 = $\frac{153}{1000}$

19) .06 = $\frac{6}{100}$ 20) .01 = $\frac{1}{100}$ 21) .37 = $\frac{37}{100}$

22) .49 = $\frac{49}{100}$ 23) .848 = $\frac{848}{1000}$ 24) .459 = $\frac{459}{1000}$

Convert the fractions to decimals.

1) $\frac{380}{1000}$ = .38   2) $\frac{7}{10}$ = .7   3) $\frac{4}{10}$ = .4

4) $\frac{69}{100}$ = .69   5) $\frac{2}{10}$ = .2   6) $\frac{8}{10}$ = .8

7) $\frac{35}{100}$ = .35   8) $\frac{62}{1000}$ = .062   9) $\frac{5}{10}$ = .5

10) $\frac{1}{10}$ = .1   11) $\frac{57}{100}$ = .57   12) $\frac{763}{1000}$ = .763

Convert the decimals to fractions. Write as 10ths, 100ths or 1000ths.

13) .6 = $\frac{6}{10}$ 14) .021 = $\frac{21}{1000}$ 15) .902 = $\frac{902}{1000}$

16) .8 = $\frac{8}{10}$ 17) .1 = $\frac{1}{10}$ 18) .031 = $\frac{31}{1000}$

19) .07 = $\frac{7}{100}$ 20) .4 = $\frac{4}{10}$ 21) .01 = $\frac{1}{100}$

22) .974 = $\frac{974}{1000}$ 23) .853 = $\frac{853}{1000}$ 24) .2 = $\frac{2}{10}$

Multiply.

1) 62 x .001 = .062   2) 426 x .1 = 42.6

3) 705 x .001 = .705   4) 55 x .1 = 5.5

5) 81 x .001 = .081   6) 63 x .001 = .063

7) 95 x .1 = 9.5   8) 844 x .001 = .844

9) 475 x .1 = 47.5   10) 364 x .01 = 3.64

11) 88 x .1 = 8.8   12) 445 x .001 = .445

Fill in the blanks with .1, .01 or .001 to make the statements correct.

13) 476 x .01 = 4.76   14) 407 x .01 = 4.07

15) 66 x .001 = .066   16) 990 x .001 = .99

17) 881 x .001 = .881   18) 428 x .01 = 4.28

19) 64 x .1 = 6.4   20) 180 x .01 = 1.8

21) 123 x .01 = 1.23   22) 76 x .001 = .076

23) 175 x .1 = 17.5   24) 185 x .01 = 1.85

Multiply.

1) 57 x .001 = .057   2) 194 x .01 = 1.94

3) 13 x .1 = 1.3   4) 261 x .001 = .261

5) 967 x .001 = .967   6) 845 x .001 = .845

7) 482 x .1 = 48.2   8) 636 x .001 = .636

9) 988 x .001 = .988   10) 50 x .1 = 5

11) 872 x .1 = 87.2   12) 56 x .001 = .056

Fill in the blanks with .1, .01 or .001 to make the statements correct.

13) 16 x .01 = .16   14) 192 x .001 = .192

15) 56 x .01 = .56   16) 624 x .01 = 6.24

17) 318 x .01 = 3.18   18) 254 x .001 = .254

19) 511 x .01 = 5.11   20) 662 x .1 = 66.2

21) 42 x .1 = 4.2   22) 809 x .01 = 8.09

23) 824 x .01 = 8.24   24) 75 x .001 = .075

Multiply.

1) 312 x .01 = 3.12   2) 405 x .001 = .405
3) 100 x .1 = 10   4) 386 x .01 = 3.86
5) 172 x .01 = 1.72   6) 375 x .1 = 37.5
7) 939 x .01 = 9.39   8) 96 x .001 = .096
9) 21 x .01 = .21   10) 685 x .1 = 68.5
11) 860 x .1 = 86   12) 672 x .001 = .672

Fill in the blanks with .1, .01 or .001 to make the statements correct.

13) 22 x .01 = .22   14) 74 x .1 = 7.4
15) 29 x .001 = .029   16) 67 x .1 = 6.7
17) 77 x .01 = .77   18) 652 x .001 = .652
19) 646 x .001 = .646   20) 642 x .01 = 6.42
21) 35 x .1 = 3.5   22) 26 x .01 = .26
23) 834 x .001 = .834   24) 849 x .001 = .849

Multiply.

1) 412 x .01 = 4.12   2) 145 x .001 = .145
3) 775 x .001 = .775   4) 85 x .001 = .085
5) 844 x .01 = 8.44   6) 24 x .001 = .024
7) 43 x .1 = 4.3   8) 421 x .001 = .421
9) 81 x .001 = .081   10) 463 x .01 = 4.63
11) 537 x .001 = .537   12) 62 x .1 = 6.2

Fill in the blanks with .1, .01 or .001 to make the statements correct.

13) 404 x .001 = .404   14) 21 x .1 = 2.1
15) 869 x .1 = 86.9   16) 16 x .1 = 1.6
17) 122 x .001 = .122   18) 56 x .01 = .56
19) 697 x .1 = 69.7   20) 88 x .1 = 8.8
21) 96 x .001 = .096   22) 619 x .001 = .619
23) 702 x .1 = 70.2   24) 766 x .001 = .766

Multiply.

1) 862 x .1 = 86.2   2) 749 x .1 = 74.9
3) 740 x .1 = 74   4) 55 x .01 = .55
5) 773 x .01 = 7.73   6) 463 x .001 = .463
7) 570 x .1 = 57   8) 27 x .001 = .027
9) 37 x .1 = 3.7   10) 22 x .1 = 2.2
11) 424 x .01 = 4.24   12) 24 x .001 = .024

Fill in the blanks with .1, .01 or .001 to make the statements correct.

13) 833 x .01 = 8.33   14) 860 x .1 = 86
15) 643 x .1 = 64.3   16) 611 x .01 = 6.11
17) 58 x .01 = .58   18) 168 x .1 = 16.8
19) 96 x .001 = .096   20) 922 x .001 = .922
21) 84 x .01 = .84   22) 742 x .1 = 74.2
23) 250 x .1 = 25   24) 61 x .001 = .061

Multiply.

1) 70 x .1 = 7   2) 833 x .001 = .833
3) 20 x .001 = .02   4) 132 x .001 = .132
5) 22 x .01 = .22   6) 914 x .1 = 91.4
7) 46 x .01 = .46   8) 678 x .001 = .678
9) 491 x .1 = 49.1   10) 640 x .1 = 64
11) 59 x .1 = 5.9   12) 75 x .1 = 7.5

Fill in the blanks with .1, .01 or .001 to make the statements correct.

13) 29 x .001 = .029   14) 23 x .001 = .023
15) 98 x .01 = .98   16) 48 x .01 = .48
17) 15 x .1 = 1.5   18) 344 x .01 = 3.44
19) 17 x .01 = .17   20) 42 x .001 = .042
21) 699 x .1 = 69.9   22) 295 x .1 = 29.5
23) 435 x .1 = 43.5   24) 76 x .01 = .76

Multiply.

1) 64 x .001 = .064   2) 882 x .1 = 88.2
3) 24 x .01 = .24   4) 624 x .001 = .624
5) 93 x .1 = 9.3   6) 21 x .001 = .021
7) 143 x .1 = 14.3   8) 30 x .1 = 3
9) 661 x .01 = 6.61   10) 885 x .001 = .885
11) 927 x .001 = .927   12) 826 x .01 = 8.26

Fill in the blanks with .1, .01 or .001 to make the statements correct.

13) 98 x .1 = 9.8   14) 816 x .01 = 8.16
15) 19 x .01 = .19   16) 723 x .01 = 7.23
17) 85 x .001 = .085   18) 44 x .1 = 4.4
19) 17 x .001 = .017   20) 29 x .01 = .29
21) 157 x .001 = .157   22) 712 x .1 = 71.2
23) 25 x .1 = 2.5   24) 883 x .001 = .883

Multiply.

1) 187 x .01 = 1.87   2) 11 x .01 = .11
3) 45 x .1 = 4.5   4) 63 x .01 = .63
5) 522 x .001 = .522   6) 769 x .1 = 76.9
7) 31 x .001 = .031   8) 742 x .01 = 7.42
9) 96 x .01 = .96   10) 444 x .01 = 4.44
11) 359 x .01 = 3.59   12) 250 x .1 = 25

Fill in the blanks with .1, .01 or .001 to make the statements correct.

13) 85 x .1 = 8.5   14) 150 x .001 = .15
15) 515 x .001 = .515   16) 487 x .01 = 4.87
17) 550 x .001 = .55   18) 262 x .001 = .262
19) 922 x .1 = 92.2   20) 50 x .01 = .5
21) 24 x .001 = .024   22) 465 x .01 = 4.65
23) 63 x .001 = .063   24) 753 x .01 = 7.53

www.claymaze.com

Multiply.

1) 55 x .01 = .55
2) 743 x .001 = .743
3) 21 x .1 = 2.1
4) 14 x .01 = .14
5) 277 x .01 = 2.77
6) 259 x .01 = 2.59
7) 44 x .1 = 4.4
8) 29 x .01 = .29
9) 987 x .1 = 98.7
10) 49 x .01 = .49
11) 32 x .01 = .32
12) 81 x .001 = .081

Fill in the blanks with .1, .01 or .001 to make the statements correct.

13) 755 x .01 = 7.55
14) 217 x .01 = 2.17
15) 50 x .001 = .05
16) 54 x .1 = 5.4
17) 69 x .001 = .069
18) 780 x .001 = .78
19) 27 x .001 = .027
20) 812 x .001 = .812
21) 36 x .01 = .36
22) 249 x .01 = 2.49
23) 364 x .1 = 36.4
24) 277 x .001 = .277

Multiply.

1) 77 x .01 = .77
2) 702 x .1 = 70.2
3) 88 x .001 = .088
4) 51 x .01 = .51
5) 94 x .1 = 9.4
6) 85 x .001 = .085
7) 744 x .01 = 7.44
8) 339 x .001 = .339
9) 776 x .001 = .776
10) 49 x .01 = .49
11) 32 x .01 = .32
12) 298 x .1 = 29.8

Fill in the blanks with .1, .01 or .001 to make the statements correct.

13) 28 x .01 = .28
14) 557 x .1 = 55.7
15) 209 x .01 = 2.09
16) 400 x .01 = 4
17) 63 x .001 = .063
18) 201 x .1 = 20.1
19) 22 x .001 = .022
20) 84 x .01 = .84
21) 37 x .001 = .037
22) 45 x .1 = 4.5
23) 591 x .1 = 59.1
24) 170 x .001 = .17

Multiply.

1) 260 x .01 = 2.6
2) 325 x .01 = 3.25
3) 406 x .1 = 40.6
4) 973 x .001 = .973
5) 687 x .001 = .687
6) 64 x .01 = .64
7) 540 x .01 = 5.4
8) 657 x .1 = 65.7
9) 44 x .001 = .044
10) 31 x .01 = .31
11) 49 x .1 = 4.9
12) 55 x .001 = .055

Fill in the blanks with .1, .01 or .001 to make the statements correct.

13) 863 x .01 = 8.63
14) 869 x .001 = .869
15) 855 x .001 = .855
16) 14 x .001 = .014
17) 165 x .001 = .165
18) 840 x .001 = .84
19) 23 x .01 = .23
20) 25 x .1 = 2.5
21) 734 x .1 = 73.4
22) 421 x .01 = 4.21
23) 303 x .001 = .303
24) 51 x .01 = .51

Multiply.

1) .2 x 10 = 2
2) .038 x 10 = .38
3) .38 x 10 = 3.8
4) .049 x 1000 = 49
5) 2.1 x 100 = 210
6) .15 x 1000 = 150
7) .015 x 1000 = 15
8) 9.1 x 100 = 910
9) .67 x 10 = 6.7
10) 7.7 x 100 = 770
11) .73 x 100 = 73
12) .68 x 100 = 68

Fill in the blanks with 10, 100 or 1000 to make the statements correct.

13) .032 x 1000 = 32
14) .63 x 100 = 63
15) .098 x 100 = 9.8
16) .099 x 100 = 9.9
17) 7.7 x 10 = 77
18) .2 x 100 = 20
19) .047 x 100 = 4.7
20) .057 x 1000 = 57
21) .65 x 1000 = 650
22) .48 x 10 = 4.8
23) .27 x 1000 = 270
24) .4 x 100 = 40

Multiply.

1) 3.7 x 10 = 37
2) 7.4 x 100 = 740
3) .39 x 100 = 39
4) .89 x 100 = 89
5) .032 x 10 = .32
6) .62 x 100 = 62
7) .32 x 100 = 32
8) .076 x 100 = 7.6
9) .038 x 1000 = 38
10) .38 x 100 = 38
11) .095 x 100 = 9.5
12) .67 x 10 = 6.7

Fill in the blanks with 10, 100 or 1000 to make the statements correct.

13) .91 x 1000 = 910
14) .012 x 1000 = 12
15) .063 x 10 = .63
16) .59 x 1000 = 590
17) .037 x 1000 = 37
18) .97 x 1000 = 970
19) 9.1 x 10 = 91
20) .062 x 10 = .62
21) .032 x 1000 = 32
22) .084 x 100 = 8.4
23) .6 x 10 = 6
24) .074 x 10 = .74

Multiply.

1) .095 x 100 = 9.5
2) .16 x 100 = 16
3) 7.5 x 100 = 750
4) 2.5 x 10 = 25
5) .049 x 10 = .49
6) .092 x 1000 = 92
7) .52 x 10 = 5.2
8) .19 x 10 = 1.9
9) .031 x 10 = .31
10) .13 x 1000 = 130
11) .15 x 10 = 1.5
12) .24 x 1000 = 240

Fill in the blanks with 10, 100 or 1000 to make the statements correct.

13) .054 x 100 = 5.4
14) .77 x 1000 = 770
15) .88 x 1000 = 880
16) .23 x 100 = 23
17) .53 x 1000 = 530
18) .91 x 1000 = 910
19) .71 x 10 = 7.1
20) .067 x 10 = .67
21) .51 x 10 = 5.1
22) .33 x 1000 = 330
23) 5.2 x 100 = 520
24) .078 x 1000 = 78

www.claymaze.com

PAGE: 113

Multiply.

1) .075 x 100 = 7.5
2) .027 x 1000 = 27
3) .48 x 1000 = 480
4) 2.1 x 10 = 21
5) .077 x 100 = 7.7
6) .26 x 100 = 26
7) .093 x 1000 = 93
8) .053 x 1000 = 53
9) .73 x 10 = 7.3
10) 9.4 x 10 = 94
11) .075 x 10 = .75
12) .33 x 100 = 33

Fill in the blanks with 10, 100 or 1000 to make the statements correct.

13) .52 x 100 = 52
14) .031 x 100 = 3.1
15) .62 x 100 = 62
16) 8.1 x 100 = 810
17) .081 x 100 = 8.1
18) .6 x 1000 = 600
19) 3.7 x 10 = 37
20) .06 x 100 = 6
21) .2 x 10 = 2
22) .12 x 10 = 1.2
23) .091 x 100 = 9.1
24) .62 x 10 = 6.2

PAGE: 114

Multiply.

1) .091 x 100 = 9.1
2) .31 x 10 = 3.1
3) .2 x 10 = 2
4) 9.5 x 100 = 950
5) .099 x 10 = .99
6) .79 x 100 = 79
7) .48 x 100 = 48
8) .083 x 100 = 8.3
9) .014 x 10 = .14
10) .61 x 1000 = 610
11) .43 x 10 = 4.3
12) 1.6 x 100 = 160

Fill in the blanks with 10, 100 or 1000 to make the statements correct.

13) .077 x 1000 = 77
14) 4.2 x 10 = 42
15) .012 x 1000 = 12
16) 7.4 x 100 = 740
17) .76 x 1000 = 760
18) .031 x 100 = 3.1
19) .06 x 1000 = 60
20) .016 x 1000 = 16
21) .72 x 100 = 72
22) .061 x 100 = 6.1
23) .92 x 100 = 92
24) .64 x 10 = 6.4

PAGE: 115

Multiply.

1) .047 x 100 = 4.7
2) .084 x 1000 = 84
3) .08 x 10 = .8
4) .81 x 100 = 81
5) .033 x 1000 = 33
6) .45 x 10 = 4.5
7) .062 x 10 = .62
8) 2.1 x 10 = 21
9) .27 x 10 = 2.7
10) .041 x 1000 = 41
11) .48 x 10 = 4.8
12) .49 x 1000 = 490

Fill in the blanks with 10, 100 or 1000 to make the statements correct.

13) .03 x 10 = .3
14) .015 x 10 = .15
15) .88 x 1000 = 880
16) 6.4 x 100 = 640
17) .91 x 1000 = 910
18) .3 x 100 = 30
19) .075 x 100 = 7.5
20) .26 x 10 = 2.6
21) 5.4 x 10 = 54
22) .028 x 1000 = 28
23) .59 x 100 = 59
24) .74 x 1000 = 740

PAGE: 116

Multiply.

1) .061 x 1000 = 61
2) .023 x 100 = 2.3
3) .11 x 1000 = 110
4) .32 x 100 = 32
5) .81 x 1000 = 810
6) 8.5 x 10 = 85
7) .048 x 10 = .48
8) .31 x 10 = 3.1
9) 8.9 x 10 = 89
10) .38 x 100 = 38
11) 9.4 x 100 = 940
12) .056 x 1000 = 56

Fill in the blanks with 10, 100 or 1000 to make the statements correct.

13) .46 x 100 = 46
14) .08 x 10 = .8
15) 6.2 x 100 = 620
16) 9.5 x 10 = 95
17) .42 x 1000 = 420
18) 5.4 x 10 = 54
19) .031 x 100 = 3.1
20) .5 x 1000 = 500
21) .055 x 1000 = 55
22) 2.1 x 100 = 210
23) .047 x 10 = .47
24) .62 x 10 = 6.2

PAGE: 117

Multiply.

1) 2.6 x 10 = 26
2) .15 x 10 = 1.5
3) .26 x 10 = 2.6
4) .032 x 1000 = 32
5) 4.2 x 100 = 420
6) .61 x 100 = 61
7) 1.8 x 100 = 180
8) .74 x 100 = 74
9) .079 x 10 = .79
10) .097 x 100 = 9.7
11) .21 x 10 = 2.1
12) .51 x 1000 = 510

Fill in the blanks with 10, 100 or 1000 to make the statements correct.

13) .094 x 100 = 9.4
14) .61 x 1000 = 610
15) 5.7 x 10 = 57
16) .055 x 1000 = 55
17) .85 x 100 = 85
18) .64 x 10 = 6.4
19) 7.7 x 100 = 770
20) .019 x 1000 = 19
21) .86 x 10 = 8.6
22) .54 x 100 = 54
23) .085 x 100 = 8.5
24) .027 x 1000 = 27

PAGE: 118

Multiply.

1) .16 x 10 = 1.6
2) .44 x 1000 = 440
3) .5 x 1000 = 500
4) .05 x 10 = .5
5) 1.6 x 10 = 16
6) .091 x 1000 = 91
7) .092 x 1000 = 92
8) .6 x 1000 = 600
9) .08 x 100 = 8
10) 4.2 x 10 = 42
11) .015 x 1000 = 15
12) .025 x 100 = 2.5

Fill in the blanks with 10, 100 or 1000 to make the statements correct.

13) .96 x 100 = 96
14) .082 x 1000 = 82
15) .31 x 10 = 3.1
16) .36 x 1000 = 360
17) .9 x 100 = 90
18) .037 x 1000 = 37
19) 7.5 x 100 = 750
20) .88 x 10 = 8.8
21) .92 x 100 = 92
22) .047 x 10 = .47
23) .098 x 10 = .98
24) 4.2 x 100 = 420

www.claymaze.com

Multiply.

1) .096 x 1000 = 96
2) .024 x 10 = .24
3) .31 x 100 = 31
4) .097 x 1000 = 97
5) 3.7 x 10 = 37
6) .89 x 100 = 89
7) .011 x 1000 = 11
8) .05 x 10 = .5
9) .062 x 10 = .62
10) 4.1 x 100 = 410
11) .36 x 100 = 36
12) .055 x 100 = 5.5

Fill in the blanks with 10, 100 or 1000 to make the statements correct.

13) .74 x 10 = 7.4
14) .056 x 10 = .56
15) .84 x 1000 = 840
16) .044 x 1000 = 44
17) .77 x 1000 = 770
18) .48 x 100 = 48
19) .76 x 100 = 76
20) 8.6 x 100 = 860
21) .038 x 10 = .38
22) .53 x 1000 = 530
23) .058 x 1000 = 58
24) .93 x 10 = 9.3

Multiply.

1) .056 x 10 = .56
2) 4.2 x 100 = 420
3) .45 x 100 = 45
4) .76 x 100 = 76
5) .34 x 100 = 34
6) .2 x 1000 = 200
7) .39 x 100 = 39
8) 6.2 x 10 = 62
9) .016 x 1000 = 16
10) .08 x 10 = .8
11) 8.4 x 10 = 84
12) .064 x 10 = .64

Fill in the blanks with 10, 100 or 1000 to make the statements correct.

13) .019 x 1000 = 19
14) 7.5 x 100 = 750
15) 2.1 x 100 = 210
16) .022 x 1000 = 22
17) .055 x 1000 = 55
18) .02 x 10 = .2
19) .27 x 100 = 27
20) .74 x 10 = 7.4
21) .03 x 1000 = 30
22) .025 x 100 = 2.5
23) .037 x 1000 = 37
24) .22 x 10 = 2.2

1) 63.15
   + 4.2
  ─────
   67.35

2) 14
  +45.28
  ─────
   59.28

3) 6.79
  +61.1
  ─────
   67.89

4) 9.4
  +53.18
  ─────
   62.58

5) 6.2
  +21.34
  ─────
   27.54

6) 59.55
  + .16
  ─────
   59.71

7) 3.36
  +27.2
  ─────
   30.56

8) 46.11
  + .26
  ─────
   46.37

9) 33
  - 4.7
  ─────
   28.3

10) 94.02
  -86.14
  ─────
   7.88

11) 39.49
  - 6.7
  ─────
   32.79

12) 83.41
  -82.7
  ─────
   .71

13) 72.31
  - .11
  ─────
   72.20

14) 43.13
  - 2.4
  ─────
   40.73

15) 28.34
  - 5.7
  ─────
   22.64

16) 65.08
  -57.18
  ─────
   7.90

17) 46 + 39.67 = 85.67
18) 30.2 - 26.41 = 3.79

1) 17.37
  + 1.5
  ─────
   18.87

2) 27.7
  +42.77
  ─────
   70.47

3) 8.82
  +73.86
  ─────
   82.68

4) 6.22
  +75.5
  ─────
   81.72

5) 3.7
  +62.26
  ─────
   65.96

6) 23.8
  +14.44
  ─────
   38.24

7) 18.8
  +33.56
  ─────
   52.36

8) 16
  +59.69
  ─────
   75.69

9) 18.55
  - 2.4
  ─────
   16.15

10) 48.57
  -44.07
  ─────
   4.50

11) 61
  -34.68
  ─────
   26.32

12) 84.63
  - 1.2
  ─────
   83.43

13) 73.19
  - .24
  ─────
   72.95

14) 59.75
  -24.75
  ─────
   35.00

15) 20.26
  - 1.6
  ─────
   18.66

16) 42
  - 4.31
  ─────
   37.69

17) .76 + 59.4 = 60.16
18) 60.95 - 2.5 = 58.45

1) 45.8
  +50.26
  ─────
   96.06

2) 1.35
  +65.5
  ─────
   66.85

3) .73
  +75.8
  ─────
   76.53

4) 8.9
  +59.27
  ─────
   68.17

5) 13.6
  +24.62
  ─────
   38.22

6) .91
  +36.5
  ─────
   37.41

7) 24.53
  + 3.65
  ─────
   28.18

8) 3.2
  +74.83
  ─────
   78.03

9) 24.15
  -17.75
  ─────
   6.40

10) 77.6
  - 1.88
  ─────
   75.72

11) 43.24
  - 8.6
  ─────
   34.64

12) 85.72
  -49.75
  ─────
   35.97

13) 48
  - 4.98
  ─────
   43.02

14) 21.07
  -20.3
  ─────
   .77

15) 63.93
  -59.23
  ─────
   4.70

16) 60.43
  - .46
  ─────
   59.97

17) 59.35 + 26 = 85.35
18) 62 - 8.18 = 53.82

1) 9.64
  +28.1
  ─────
   37.74

2) 13.3
  +17.37
  ─────
   30.67

3) 44.6
  +46.68
  ─────
   91.28

4) .27
  +24.21
  ─────
   24.48

5) 38.65
  + .64
  ─────
   39.29

6) 9.4
  +42.83
  ─────
   52.23

7) 23.03
  + 4.97
  ─────
   28.00

8) 9.5
  +59.59
  ─────
   69.09

9) 44.1
  - 3.89
  ─────
   40.21

10) 46.86
  - 5.9
  ─────
   40.96

11) 31.29
  -23.27
  ─────
   8.02

12) 98
  -73.58
  ─────
   24.42

13) 30.09
  -27.59
  ─────
   2.50

14) 29
  - 3.52
  ─────
   25.48

15) 16.02
  - 1.4
  ─────
   14.62

16) 49.96
  -44.46
  ─────
   5.50

17) 7.03 + 83.2 = 90.23
18) 15.82 - .23 = 15.59

PAGE: 126

1) 32.53 + .74 33.27	2) 5.4 +59.72 65.12	3) 46.2 +27.34 73.54	4) 1.52 +16.8 18.32
5) 5.2 +62.59 67.79	6) 2.5 +32.53 35.03	7) 43 +11.08 54.08	8) 8.9 +32.74 41.64
9) 46.07 - 5.2 40.87	10) 24.8 - .59 24.21	11) 68 -45.82 22.18	12) 54.73 -53.16 1.57
13) 57.32 - .9 56.42	14) 74 -28.06 45.94	15) 72.83 -29.93 42.90	16) 81.17 - 7.5 73.67

17) 14 + 47.41 = 61.41   18) 30.4 - 5.95 = 24.45

PAGE: 127

1) 8.6 +87.42 96.02	2) 17.62 + 5.7 23.32	3) 73.88 + 5.65 79.53	4) 52.86 + .17 53.03
5) 6.95 +11.5 18.45	6) 1.8 +60.56 62.36	7) .87 +33.6 34.47	8) 7.67 +91.1 98.77
9) 47.92 -46.32 1.60	10) 55 -47.61 7.39	11) 70.69 - 6.9 63.79	12) 40.03 -35.53 4.50
13) 58.2 -57.67 .53	14) 23.1 - 4.01 19.09	15) 70 -62.35 7.65	16) 68.2 - 6.04 62.16

17) 7.33 + 14 = 21.33   18) 47.75 - .98 = 46.77

PAGE: 128

1) 28.53 +59.1 87.63	2) 29.24 + 3.62 32.86	3) 62.1 +15.75 77.85	4) 15.4 +34.39 49.79
5) 21.7 +69.58 91.28	6) 2.1 +17.93 20.03	7) 8.41 +85.5 93.91	8) 30.01 + 8.18 38.19
9) 68 - 3.67 64.33	10) 23.11 -20.61 2.50	11) 58.91 - 4.4 54.51	12) 51.62 - .83 50.79
13) 96.19 - 6.7 89.49	14) 71.21 - 8.1 63.11	15) 84 -59.25 24.75	16) 35.39 -28.53 6.86

17) 12 + 46.41 = 58.41   18) 26.24 - 5.01 = 21.23

PAGE: 129

1) 52.6 +28.29 80.89	2) 15.16 + 6.5 21.66	3) 9.1 +50.04 59.14	4) 86 +13.72 99.72
5) 3.1 +58.47 61.57	6) 35.6 +14.15 49.75	7) 5.5 +41.74 47.24	8) 6.29 +13.15 19.44
9) 58 -10.09 47.91	10) 36.75 - 6.5 30.25	11) 82.8 -28.58 54.22	12) 37 -11.74 25.26
13) 97.72 -52.72 45.00	14) 89.1 -48.03 41.07	15) 75.57 - 5.5 70.07	16) 20.61 -15.41 5.20

17) .77 + 68 = 68.77   18) 81.2 - 27.65 = 53.55

PAGE: 130

1) 2.54 +38.1 40.64	2) 13 +46.42 59.42	3) 41.04 + 7.7 48.74	4) .24 +93.2 93.44
5) 67.55 + 7.15 74.70	6) 50.36 + .31 50.67	7) 19.2 +77.56 96.76	8) .79 +36.93 37.72
9) 42.07 -34.17 7.90	10) 27.1 -26.55 .55	11) 64 - .49 63.51	12) 23.46 -18.25 5.21
13) 57.47 -15.1 42.37	14) 74.52 -60.57 13.95	15) 75.2 -38.97 36.23	16) 97 -64.49 32.51

17) 3.32 + 15.74 = 19.06   18) 98.3 - 38.35 = 59.95

PAGE: 131

1) 17.79 + 4.78 22.57	2) 1.3 +29.89 31.19	3) 43.8 +11.73 55.53	4) 26.27 + 1.5 27.77
5) 54.78 + 3.85 58.63	6) .85 +38.58 39.43	7) 2.1 +86.09 88.19	8) 5.93 +30.42 36.35
9) 79 -45.21 33.79	10) 84.54 - .92 83.62	11) 81.5 -57.36 24.14	12) 51.17 -22.19 28.98
13) 90.27 - 7.62 82.65	14) 28.9 - 3.76 25.14	15) 49.21 -47.68 1.53	16) 65.4 -22.75 42.65

17) 4.74 + 21.23 = 25.97   18) 42 - 28.53 = 13.47

1) $60.65 + .38 = 61.03$
2) $1.5 + 48.93 = 50.43$
3) $14 + 79.52 = 93.52$
4) $59.8 + 22.94 = 82.74$
5) $6.5 + 49.41 = 55.91$
6) $15.25 + .73 = 15.98$
7) $6.4 + 28.52 = 34.92$
8) $8.27 + 19.7 = 27.97$
9) $81.46 - 27.23 = 54.23$
10) $20 - 19.89 = .11$
11) $62.83 - 3.48 = 59.35$
12) $74.05 - .08 = 73.97$
13) $16 - 12.22 = 3.78$
14) $20.14 - 19.28 = .86$
15) $34.1 - 2.03 = 32.07$
16) $18.24 - 14.54 = 3.70$

17) $3.2 + 21.69 = 24.89$
18) $76.8 - 32.78 = 44.02$

Multiply.
1) $.4 \times .3 = .12$
2) $.7 \times 9 = 6.3$
3) $5 \times .4 = 2.0$
4) $.5 \times .5 = .25$
5) $.6 \times .6 = .36$
6) $.7 \times 2 = 1.4$
7) $.4 \times .6 = .24$
8) $4 \times .2 = .8$
9) $.6 \times .7 = .42$
10) $8 \times .5 = 4.0$
11) $9 \times .4 = 3.6$
12) $.9 \times 3 = 2.7$
13) $.5 \times .2 = .1$
14) $.2 \times 4 = .8$
15) $.3 \times .6 = .18$

Multiply.
16) $3.7 \times 8 = 29.6$
17) $98 \times .2 = 19.6$
18) $7.5 \times 4 = 30.0$
19) $49 \times .5 = 24.5$
20) $3.6 \times .9 = 3.24$
21) $2.7 \times 4 = 10.8$
22) $5.7 \times 5 = 28.5$
23) $2.5 \times .9 = 2.25$
24) $2.6 \times 4 = 10.4$
25) $39 \times .9 = 35.1$
26) $37 \times .5 = 18.5$
27) $25 \times .4 = 10.0$

Multiply.
1) $2 \times .3 = .6$
2) $.7 \times .9 = .63$
3) $.8 \times .5 = .4$
4) $.5 \times 7 = 3.5$
5) $.2 \times 8 = 1.6$
6) $8 \times .9 = 7.2$
7) $5 \times .4 = 2.0$
8) $.5 \times .6 = .3$
9) $6 \times .5 = 3.0$
10) $.3 \times 4 = 1.2$
11) $9 \times .8 = 7.2$
12) $.3 \times .3 = .09$
13) $.6 \times .7 = .42$
14) $.4 \times 4 = 1.6$
15) $.5 \times .9 = .45$

Multiply.
16) $2.7 \times .8 = 2.16$
17) $20 \times .5 = 10.0$
18) $7.4 \times 7 = 51.8$
19) $81 \times .9 = 72.9$
20) $54 \times .4 = 21.6$
21) $98 \times .2 = 19.6$
22) $33 \times .5 = 16.5$
23) $57 \times .8 = 45.6$
24) $28 \times .9 = 25.2$
25) $55 \times .3 = 16.5$
26) $2.2 \times 9 = 19.8$
27) $1.5 \times .5 = .75$

Multiply.
1) $.9 \times .6 = .54$
2) $.6 \times .2 = .12$
3) $.3 \times .8 = .24$
4) $.4 \times .3 = .12$
5) $.7 \times .9 = .63$
6) $2 \times .6 = 1.2$
7) $.7 \times 9 = 6.3$
8) $.5 \times .6 = .3$
9) $5 \times .4 = 2.0$
10) $.3 \times .6 = .18$
11) $.7 \times .3 = .21$
12) $.2 \times .5 = .1$
13) $5 \times .7 = 3.5$
14) $.4 \times .5 = .2$
15) $.8 \times .6 = .48$

Multiply.
16) $6.7 \times .4 = 2.68$
17) $5.7 \times 7 = 39.9$
18) $62 \times .4 = 24.8$
19) $9.8 \times 2 = 19.6$
20) $2.6 \times 4 = 10.4$
21) $58 \times .5 = 29.0$
22) $90 \times .9 = 81.0$
23) $42 \times .5 = 21.0$
24) $17 \times .9 = 15.3$
25) $5.9 \times 5 = 29.5$
26) $2.5 \times 4 = 10.0$
27) $52 \times .2 = 10.4$

Multiply.
1) $.4 \times 8 = 3.2$
2) $.5 \times .9 = .45$
3) $.9 \times 4 = 3.6$
4) $.2 \times .5 = .1$
5) $.7 \times .6 = .42$
6) $.6 \times .3 = .18$
7) $.9 \times .6 = .54$
8) $.6 \times .5 = .3$
9) $.2 \times .6 = .12$
10) $.3 \times .7 = .21$
11) $2 \times .4 = .8$
12) $.5 \times .3 = .15$
13) $6 \times .9 = 5.4$
14) $.6 \times .7 = .42$
15) $.9 \times .9 = .81$

Multiply.
16) $5.7 \times 8 = 45.6$
17) $98 \times .5 = 49.0$
18) $8.4 \times 4 = 33.6$
19) $90 \times .4 = 36.0$
20) $29 \times .5 = 14.5$
21) $4.3 \times .2 = .86$
22) $12 \times .9 = 10.8$
23) $64 \times .2 = 12.8$
24) $21 \times .8 = 16.8$
25) $4.7 \times .9 = 4.23$
26) $4.3 \times .5 = 2.15$
27) $89 \times .4 = 35.6$

Multiply.
1) $.7 \times .5 = .35$
2) $.3 \times .4 = .12$
3) $.2 \times .3 = .06$
4) $.9 \times .9 = .81$
5) $.6 \times .5 = .3$
6) $.3 \times .9 = .27$
7) $.6 \times .4 = .24$
8) $8 \times .3 = 2.4$
9) $.9 \times 7 = 6.3$
10) $.3 \times .3 = .09$
11) $.9 \times 9 = 8.1$
12) $.4 \times .3 = .12$
13) $.6 \times 8 = 4.8$
14) $.8 \times .3 = .24$
15) $5 \times .6 = 3.0$

Multiply.
16) $1.8 \times 2 = 3.6$
17) $75 \times .4 = 30.0$
18) $44 \times .2 = 8.8$
19) $1.8 \times 7 = 12.6$
20) $2.2 \times 5 = 11.0$
21) $2.1 \times 8 = 16.8$
22) $87 \times .5 = 43.5$
23) $5.2 \times .2 = 1.04$
24) $47 \times .4 = 18.8$
25) $70 \times .5 = 35.0$
26) $23 \times .9 = 20.7$
27) $4.7 \times 5 = 23.5$

www.claymaze.com

PAGE: 139

Multiply.

1) .5 x .7 = .35   2) .6 x .5 = .3   3) .3 x .9 = .27

4) .9 x 4 = 3.6   5) .7 x .9 = .63   6) .5 x 4 = 2.0

7) .6 x .2 = .12   8) 4 x .8 = 3.2   9) .6 x .9 = .54

10) 8 x .7 = 5.6   11) .6 x .6 = .36   12) .5 x .4 = .2

13) .3 x .8 = .24   14) .2 x 5 = 1.0   15) .3 x .6 = .18

Multiply.

16) 1.6 x 2 3.2	17) 13 x .4 5.2	18) 36 x .8 28.8	19) 3.7 x .9 3.33
20) 7.7 x 5 38.5	21) 91 x .8 72.8	22) 20 x .4 8.0	23) 2.7 x 5 13.5
24) 54 x .4 21.6	25) 59 x .5 29.5	26) 33 x .9 29.7	27) 54 x .2 10.8

PAGE: 140

Multiply.

1) 4 x .4 = 1.6   2) .2 x .6 = .12   3) .6 x .7 = .42

4) 8 x .8 = 6.4   5) .9 x .7 = .63   6) .4 x .3 = .12

7) .5 x 6 = 3.0   8) .7 x .3 = .21   9) .8 x .6 = .48

10) 5 x .3 = 1.5   11) .4 x 4 = 1.6   12) .3 x .3 = .09

13) .9 x .6 = .54   14) 9 x .2 = 1.8   15) .8 x 5 = 4.0

Multiply.

16) 5.2 x .2 1.04	17) 93 x .9 83.7	18) 3.5 x .5 1.75	19) 6.2 x 2 12.4
20) 5.5 x .5 2.75	21) 89 x .8 71.2	22) 98 x .9 88.2	23) 6.7 x 7 46.9
24) 62 x .8 49.6	25) 36 x .9 32.4	26) 6.5 x 4 26.0	27) 44 x .5 22.0

PAGE: 141

Multiply.

1) 4 x .2 = .8   2) .3 x .5 = .15   3) .6 x .4 = .24

4) .8 x .5 = .4   5) .7 x 8 = 5.6   6) .5 x .6 = .3

7) .6 x .8 = .48   8) .9 x .6 = .54   9) 9 x .2 = 1.8

10) .3 x .9 = .27   11) .5 x .5 = .25   12) .2 x 5 = 1.0

13) .5 x 6 = 3.0   14) .3 x .2 = .06   15) .7 x .5 = .35

Multiply.

16) 7.4 x .8 5.92	17) 68 x .9 61.2	18) 88 x .5 44.0	19) 83 x .2 16.6
20) 45 x .9 40.5	21) 31 x .5 15.5	22) 75 x .2 15.0	23) 94 x .5 47.0
24) 13 x .4 5.2	25) 1.8 x 8 14.4	26) 5.2 x .8 4.16	27) 73 x .9 65.7

PAGE: 142

Multiply.

1) .6 x .3 = .18   2) 9 x .2 = 1.8   3) .6 x .7 = .42

4) 2 x .5 = 1.0   5) .2 x 4 = .8   6) .3 x .4 = .12

7) .9 x 3 = 2.7   8) .7 x .3 = .21   9) .5 x .7 = .35

10) 9 x .9 = 8.1   11) .6 x .8 = .48   12) 6 x .9 = 5.4

13) .9 x .3 = .27   14) .4 x 8 = 3.2   15) .8 x .5 = .4

Multiply.

16) 5.7 x 4 22.8	17) 22 x .9 19.8	18) 57 x .5 28.5	19) 65 x .4 26.0
20) 45 x .3 13.5	21) 9.5 x 6 57.0	22) 80 x .2 16.0	23) 3.4 x .7 2.38
24) 27 x .4 10.8	25) 79 x .2 15.8	26) 7.7 x .5 3.85	27) 32 x .8 25.6

PAGE: 143

Multiply.

1) .6 x .4 = .24   2) 2 x .7 = 1.4   3) .6 x 7 = 4.2

4) .5 x 9 = 4.5   5) .4 x .5 = .2   6) .7 x 2 = 1.4

7) 3 x .9 = 2.7   8) .3 x .4 = .12   9) .6 x .7 = .42

10) .3 x .2 = .06   11) 5 x .8 = 4.0   12) .8 x .3 = .24

13) .6 x .8 = .48   14) .9 x 4 = 3.6   15) .7 x .5 = .35

Multiply.

16) 1.8 x 2 3.6	17) 1.3 x .4 .52	18) 6.5 x 6 39.0	19) 60 x .8 48.0
20) 64 x .8 51.2	21) 9.4 x 7 65.8	22) 1.8 x .9 1.62	23) 97 x .5 48.5
24) 30 x .9 27.0	25) 13 x .5 6.5	26) 57 x .4 22.8	27) 32 x .9 28.8

PAGE: 144

Multiply.

1) 2 x .2 = .4   2) .2 x .6 = .12   3) 5 x .7 = 3.5

4) .7 x .6 = .42   5) 7 x .3 = 2.1   6) .3 x .6 = .18

7) .9 x 6 = 5.4   8) 8 x .2 = 1.6   9) .5 x .5 = .25

10) .8 x 5 = 4.0   11) .3 x .5 = .15   12) 9 x .7 = 6.3

13) .3 x 2 = .6   14) 9 x .4 = 3.6   15) 4 x .5 = 2.0

Multiply.

16) 1.3 x .8 1.04	17) 5.4 x 4 21.6	18) 40 x .8 32.0	19) 3.5 x 3 10.5
20) 6.7 x .4 2.68	21) 1.1 x 2 2.2	22) 2.6 x 5 13.0	23) 21 x .7 14.7
24) 4.4 x 8 35.2	25) 2.2 x 9 19.8	26) 6.7 x .4 2.68	27) 5.5 x .7 3.85

www.claymaze.com

Multiply.

1) 441
  x .43
  189.63

2) 4.63
  x 9.8
  45.374

3) 398
  x .51
  202.98

4) 62.4
  x 2.1
  131.04

5) 1.97
  x 45
  88.65

6) 399
  x .43
  171.57

7) 140
  x 6.4
  896.0

8) 481
  x 1.1
  529.1

9) 64.8
  x 7.9
  511.92

Multiply.

1) 1.53
  x 60
  91.80

2) 35.2
  x 3.6
  126.72

3) 48.3
  x 6.5
  313.95

4) 10.3
  x .59
  6.077

5) 7.61
  x 2.7
  20.547

6) 2.47
  x 65
  160.55

7) 58.6
  x 14
  820.4

8) 62.6
  x 8.5
  532.10

9) 6.68
  x 16
  106.88

Multiply.

1) 393
  x .76
  298.68

2) 6.91
  x 9.8
  67.718

3) 13.8
  x .44
  6.072

4) 2.57
  x 21
  53.97

5) 8.85
  x 37
  327.45

6) 71.5
  x 3.1
  221.65

7) 6.22
  x 15
  93.30

8) 9.15
  x 23
  210.45

9) 9.31
  x 15
  139.65

Multiply.

1) 882
  x .39
  343.98

2) 735
  x .31
  227.85

3) 6.71
  x 58
  389.18

4) 120
  x 8.1
  972.0

5) 8.58
  x 1.8
  15.444

6) 90.1
  x 8.1
  729.81

7) 9.53
  x 7.5
  71.475

8) 71.5
  x 8.8
  629.20

9) 9.59
  x 76
  728.84

Multiply.

1) 12.9
  x .84
  10.836

2) 8.42
  x 37
  311.54

3) 2.52
  x 20
  50.40

4) 858
  x .17
  145.86

5) 8.41
  x 70
  588.70

6) 340
  x 1.8
  612.0

7) 741
  x .53
  392.73

8) 27.6
  x .84
  23.184

9) 93.2
  x 6.2
  577.84

Multiply.

1) 2.75
  x 37
  101.75

2) 822
  x .51
  419.22

3) 40.5
  x 4.2
  170.10

4) 6.53
  x 47
  306.91

5) 5.78
  x 75
  433.50

6) 729
  x .15
  109.35

7) 89.3
  x .16
  14.288

8) 483
  x .72
  347.76

9) 68.9
  x 2.2
  151.58

www.claymaze.com

Multiply.

1) 3.09 × 6.7 = 20.703	2) 47.2 × 4.2 = 198.24	3) 5.11 × 31 = 158.41
4) 9.21 × 15 = 138.15	5) 5.08 × 5.2 = 26.416	6) 6.46 × 6.4 = 41.344
7) 559 × .75 = 419.25	8) 15.3 × .54 = 8.262	9) 871 × .55 = 479.05

Multiply.

1) 5.95 × 61 = 362.95	2) 964 × .36 = 347.04	3) 779 × .25 = 194.75
4) 193 × .52 = 100.36	5) 22.5 × 7.9 = 177.75	6) 3.38 × 20 = 67.60
7) 325 × .14 = 45.50	8) 40.8 × .37 = 15.096	9) 64.4 × 5.2 = 334.88

Multiply.

1) 2.45 × 8.5 = 20.825	2) 29.2 × 6.7 = 195.64	3) 622 × .74 = 460.28
4) 7.96 × 20 = 159.20	5) 58.2 × .39 = 22.698	6) 42.4 × 3.4 = 144.16
7) 8.28 × 51 = 422.28	8) 3.92 × 3.1 = 12.152	9) 297 × .54 = 160.38

Multiply.

1) 251 × .78 = 195.78	2) 2.87 × 28 = 80.36	3) 70.4 × 4.3 = 302.72
4) 875 × .85 = 743.75	5) 28.6 × 32 = 915.2	6) 316 × .74 = 233.84
7) 83.9 × .15 = 12.585	8) 46.1 × 9.5 = 437.95	9) 218 × 4.3 = 937.4

Multiply.

1) 72.3 × 4.4 = 318.12	2) 397 × .67 = 265.99	3) 32.1 × 2.5 = 80.25
4) 849 × .24 = 203.76	5) 2.33 × 12 = 27.96	6) 39.8 × .33 = 13.134
7) 8.22 × 57 = 468.54	8) 1.18 × 4.4 = 5.192	9) 965 × .31 = 299.15

Divide.

1) 2)2.72 = 1.36	2) 6)4.38 = .73	3) 8)8.64 = 1.08	4) 5)2.75 = .55
5) 3)2.34 = .78	6) 4)6.72 = 1.68	7) 3)8.25 = 2.75	8) 7)8.96 = 1.28
9) 5)4.85 = .97	10) 2)8.96 = 4.48	11) 9)7.56 = .84	12) 4)7.32 = 1.83
13) 3)2.16 = .72	14) 6)8.76 = 1.46	15) 2)8.22 = 4.11	16) 8)6.64 = .83

www.claymaze.com

Divide.

1) $.37$; $4\overline{)1.48}$ 2) $.64$; $3\overline{)1.92}$ 3) $.69$; $7\overline{)4.83}$ 4) $.83$; $2\overline{)1.66}$

5) $.72$; $6\overline{)4.32}$ 6) 4.48 ; $2\overline{)8.96}$ 7) $.45$; $9\overline{)4.05}$ 8) 3.22 ; $3\overline{)9.66}$

9) $.91$; $2\overline{)1.82}$ 10) 1.65 ; $5\overline{)8.25}$ 11) 1.98 ; $4\overline{)7.92}$ 12) $.75$; $5\overline{)3.75}$

13) $.92$; $7\overline{)6.44}$ 14) $.68$; $3\overline{)2.04}$ 15) 2.34 ; $2\overline{)4.68}$ 16) $.61$; $3\overline{)1.83}$

Divide.

1) $.16$; $9\overline{)1.44}$ 2) $.59$; $8\overline{)4.72}$ 3) $.76$; $7\overline{)5.32}$ 4) $.86$; $6\overline{)5.16}$

5) $.64$; $4\overline{)2.56}$ 6) $.43$; $9\overline{)3.87}$ 7) 1.63 ; $6\overline{)9.78}$ 8) 2.39 ; $4\overline{)9.56}$

9) 4.64 ; $2\overline{)9.28}$ 10) $.46$; $8\overline{)3.68}$ 11) 1.54 ; $3\overline{)4.62}$ 12) $.61$; $5\overline{)3.05}$

13) $.97$; $7\overline{)6.79}$ 14) 3.49 ; $2\overline{)6.98}$ 15) $.32$; $4\overline{)1.28}$ 16) 1.87 ; $2\overline{)3.74}$

Divide.

1) $.58$; $7\overline{)4.06}$ 2) $.12$; $9\overline{)1.08}$ 3) $.26$; $4\overline{)1.04}$ 4) $.73$; $2\overline{)1.46}$

5) $.75$; $3\overline{)2.25}$ 6) $.49$; $8\overline{)3.92}$ 7) $.97$; $5\overline{)4.85}$ 8) $.17$; $6\overline{)1.02}$

9) 2.82 ; $2\overline{)5.64}$ 10) $.15$; $7\overline{)1.05}$ 11) 1.62 ; $2\overline{)3.24}$ 12) $.86$; $4\overline{)3.44}$

13) $.79$; $7\overline{)5.53}$ 14) 1.77 ; $5\overline{)8.85}$ 15) 2.74 ; $3\overline{)8.22}$ 16) $.49$; $5\overline{)2.45}$

Divide.

1) $.79$; $8\overline{)6.32}$ 2) 1.64 ; $3\overline{)4.92}$ 3) $.87$; $5\overline{)4.35}$ 4) 2.41 ; $2\overline{)4.82}$

5) $.27$; $9\overline{)2.43}$ 6) 1.33 ; $6\overline{)7.98}$ 7) 2.49 ; $2\overline{)4.98}$ 8) $.81$; $7\overline{)5.67}$

9) 2.97 ; $3\overline{)8.91}$ 10) $.86$; $7\overline{)6.02}$ 11) $.62$; $4\overline{)2.48}$ 12) $.31$; $9\overline{)2.79}$

13) $.28$; $8\overline{)2.24}$ 14) $.91$; $9\overline{)8.19}$ 15) 1.07 ; $2\overline{)2.14}$ 16) $.66$; $3\overline{)1.98}$

Divide.

1) $.59$; $7\overline{)4.13}$ 2) 1.14 ; $6\overline{)6.84}$ 3) $.56$; $8\overline{)4.48}$ 4) $.77$; $2\overline{)1.54}$

5) $.49$; $9\overline{)4.41}$ 6) 1.19 ; $3\overline{)3.57}$ 7) $.29$; $5\overline{)1.45}$ 8) $.24$; $6\overline{)1.44}$

9) 3.51 ; $2\overline{)7.02}$ 10) $.89$; $4\overline{)3.56}$ 11) $.42$; $8\overline{)3.36}$ 12) 4.52 ; $2\overline{)9.04}$

13) $.77$; $6\overline{)4.62}$ 14) $.29$; $7\overline{)2.03}$ 15) 1.95 ; $3\overline{)5.85}$ 16) $.81$; $4\overline{)3.24}$

Divide.

1) $.74$; $7\overline{)5.18}$ 2) 1.31 ; $3\overline{)3.93}$ 3) $.39$; $8\overline{)3.12}$ 4) $.55$; $9\overline{)4.95}$

5) $.48$; $3\overline{)1.44}$ 6) 1.18 ; $2\overline{)2.36}$ 7) $.59$; $6\overline{)3.54}$ 8) $.84$; $3\overline{)2.52}$

9) 1.04 ; $8\overline{)8.32}$ 10) $.36$; $6\overline{)2.16}$ 11) $.96$; $8\overline{)7.68}$ 12) $.88$; $9\overline{)7.92}$

13) $.87$; $6\overline{)5.22}$ 14) 1.47 ; $2\overline{)2.94}$ 15) $.43$; $4\overline{)1.72}$ 16) $.85$; $5\overline{)4.25}$

www.claymaze.com

Divide.

1) 4)1.92 = .48 2) 7)4.83 = .69 3) 6)1.98 = .33 4) 2)8.46 = 4.23

5) 3)9.81 = 3.27 6) 5)2.75 = .55 7) 2)4.32 = 2.16 8) 7)4.41 = .63

9) 6)3.84 = .64 10) 7)1.54 = .22 11) 3)2.25 = .75 12) 2)7.88 = 3.94

13) 9)4.32 = .48 14) 2)4.16 = 2.08 15) 4)1.04 = .26 16) 8)5.52 = .69

Divide.

1) 7)6.79 = .97 2) 6)3.54 = .59 3) 2)1.72 = .86 4) 4)5.32 = 1.33

5) 2)8.62 = 4.31 6) 5)4.75 = .95 7) 4)2.96 = .74 8) 3)7.92 = 2.64

9) 9)1.53 = .17 10) 4)2.68 = .67 11) 2)6.18 = 3.09 12) 5)2.75 = .55

13) 2)2.86 = 1.43 14) 3)8.67 = 2.89 15) 7)9.94 = 1.42 16) 3)8.22 = 2.74

Divide.

1) 8)4.64 = .58 2) 4)8.92 = 2.23 3) 9)6.57 = .73 4) 2)1.58 = .79

5) 3)1.17 = .39 6) 6)4.32 = .72 7) 7)8.82 = 1.26 8) 8)1.44 = .18

9) 7)2.31 = .33 10) 2)5.82 = 2.91 11) 5)2.05 = .41 12) 9)7.83 = .87

13) 8)3.12 = .39 14) 7)5.46 = .78 15) 2)9.92 = 4.96 16) 3)7.32 = 2.44

Divide.

1) 2)8.08 = 4.04 2) 4)8.04 = 2.01 3) 6)9.36 = 1.56 4) 4)9.68 = 2.42

5) 7)3.64 = .52 6) 2)8.88 = 4.44 7) 5)9.45 = 1.89 8) 3)2.43 = .81

9) 8)1.92 = .24 10) 9)8.64 = .96 11) 8)1.44 = .18 12) 6)7.74 = 1.29

13) 3)4.35 = 1.45 14) 2)1.56 = .78 15) 3)8.07 = 2.69 16) 2)8.86 = 4.43

Divide. (Hint: Shift the decimal to the right on both the divisor & the dividend.)

1) .4)16.08 = 40.2 2) .3)206.1 = 687 3) .6)25.74 = 42.9

4) .5)333.5 = 667 5) .9)75.96 = 84.4 6) .7)66.71 = 95.3

7) .3)17.91 = 59.7 8) .7)58.73 = 83.9 9) .3)21.39 = 71.3

Divide. (Hint: Shift the decimal to the right on both the divisor & the dividend.)

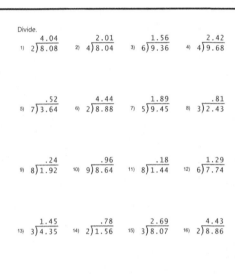

1) .6)586.8 = 978 2) .7)19.95 = 28.5 3) .6)484.2 = 807

4) .9)27.72 = 30.8 5) .4)25.76 = 64.4 6) .9)492.3 = 547

7) .6)40.38 = 67.3 8) .8)72.56 = 90.7 9) .4)182.4 = 456

www.claymaze.com

Divide. *(Hint: Shift the decimal to the right on both the divisor & the dividend.)*

1) $.3\overline{)183.6}$ quotient 612

2) $.7\overline{)27.58}$ quotient 39.4

3) $.6\overline{)495.6}$ quotient 826

4) $.2\overline{)166.4}$ quotient 832

5) $.3\overline{)28.68}$ quotient 95.6

6) $.8\overline{)441.6}$ quotient 552

7) $.7\overline{)28.14}$ quotient 40.2

8) $.5\overline{)216.5}$ quotient 433

9) $.7\overline{)589.4}$ quotient 842

Divide. *(Hint: Shift the decimal to the right on both the divisor & the dividend.)*

1) $.8\overline{)61.92}$ quotient 77.4

2) $.7\overline{)34.86}$ quotient 49.8

3) $.4\overline{)17.24}$ quotient 43.1

4) $.9\overline{)313.2}$ quotient 348

5) $.2\overline{)139.6}$ quotient 698

6) $.8\overline{)43.76}$ quotient 54.7

7) $.4\overline{)34.16}$ quotient 85.4

8) $.8\overline{)343.2}$ quotient 429

9) $.7\overline{)221.2}$ quotient 316

Divide. *(Hint: Shift the decimal to the right on both the divisor & the dividend.)*

1) $.8\overline{)51.04}$ quotient 63.8

2) $.2\overline{)19.12}$ quotient 95.6

3) $.5\overline{)38.15}$ quotient 76.3

4) $.6\overline{)223.2}$ quotient 372

5) $.7\overline{)13.58}$ quotient 19.4

6) $.9\overline{)592.2}$ quotient 658

7) $.5\overline{)48.25}$ quotient 96.5

8) $.9\overline{)20.61}$ quotient 22.9

9) $.4\overline{)11.68}$ quotient 29.2

Divide. *(Hint: Shift the decimal to the right on both the divisor & the dividend.)*

1) $.7\overline{)533.4}$ quotient 762

2) $.9\overline{)416.7}$ quotient 463

3) $.6\overline{)223.8}$ quotient 373

4) $.3\overline{)22.89}$ quotient 76.3

5) $.8\overline{)67.52}$ quotient 84.4

6) $.7\overline{)51.73}$ quotient 73.9

7) $.5\overline{)244.5}$ quotient 489

8) $.4\overline{)125.6}$ quotient 314

9) $.9\overline{)795.6}$ quotient 884

Divide. *(Hint: Shift the decimal to the right on both the divisor & the dividend.)*

1) $.6\overline{)51.84}$ quotient 86.4

2) $.2\overline{)10.18}$ quotient 50.9

3) $.3\overline{)15.93}$ quotient 53.1

4) $.7\overline{)59.92}$ quotient 85.6

5) $.8\overline{)523.2}$ quotient 654

6) $.7\overline{)32.76}$ quotient 46.8

7) $.6\overline{)18.24}$ quotient 30.4

8) $.4\overline{)38.04}$ quotient 95.1

9) $.3\overline{)180.6}$ quotient 602

Divide. *(Hint: Shift the decimal to the right on both the divisor & the dividend.)*

1) $.8\overline{)39.12}$ quotient 48.9

2) $.3\overline{)188.7}$ quotient 629

3) $.7\overline{)50.61}$ quotient 72.3

4) $.6\overline{)558.6}$ quotient 931

5) $.2\overline{)169.4}$ quotient 847

6) $.4\overline{)29.76}$ quotient 74.4

7) $.8\overline{)738.4}$ quotient 923

8) $.3\overline{)250.5}$ quotient 835

9) $.6\overline{)311.4}$ quotient 519

www.claymaze.com

Divide. *(Hint: Shift the decimal to the right on both the divisor & the dividend.)*

1) .3)239.4 = 798
2) .2)15.32 = 76.6
3) .5)25.45 = 50.9

4) .2)11.32 = 56.6
5) .6)46.26 = 77.1
6) .9)206.1 = 229

7) .6)17.46 = 29.1
8) .8)443.2 = 554
9) .3)295.8 = 986

Divide. *(Hint: Shift the decimal to the right on both the divisor & the dividend.)*

1) .7)10.43 = 14.9
2) .8)787.2 = 984
3) .9)68.94 = 76.6

4) .6)16.32 = 27.2
5) .7)61.53 = 87.9
6) .8)76.16 = 95.2

7) .5)41.95 = 83.9
8) .6)26.04 = 43.4
9) .9)81.36 = 90.4

Divide. *(Hint: Shift the decimal to the right on both the divisor & the dividend.)*

1) .8)59.28 = 74.1
2) .9)883.8 = 982
3) .5)19.65 = 39.3

4) .4)12.28 = 30.7
5) .3)21.99 = 73.3
6) .8)237.6 = 297

7) .6)250.2 = 417
8) .9)485.1 = 539
9) .7)38.78 = 55.4

Round to the nearest whole number.

1) 30.701 — 31
2) 23.824 — 24
3) 11.395 — 11
4) 41.221 — 41
5) 76.657 — 77
6) 69.514 — 70
7) 99.604 — 100
8) 65.244 — 65
9) 23.724 — 24
10) 12.318 — 12
11) 50.086 — 50
12) 41.251 — 41

Round to the nearest tenths.

13) 15.674 — 15.7
14) 89.826 — 89.8
15) 85.872 — 85.9
16) 59.489 — 59.5
17) 73.227 — 73.2
18) 43.318 — 43.3
19) 81.125 — 81.1
20) 15.288 — 15.3
21) 79.468 — 79.5
22) 45.863 — 45.9
23) 72.748 — 72.7
24) 30.372 — 30.4

Round to the nearest hundreths.

25) 42.572 — 42.57
26) 96.219 — 96.22
27) 22.368 — 22.37
28) 31.384 — 31.38
29) 13.014 — 13.01
30) 93.231 — 93.23
31) 81.916 — 81.92
32) 36.819 — 36.82
33) 89.725 — 89.73
34) 16.475 — 16.48
35) 29.172 — 29.17
36) 19.007 — 19.01

Round to the nearest whole number.

1) 87.886 — 88
2) 30.599 — 31
3) 44.823 — 45
4) 14.204 — 14
5) 33.221 — 33
6) 91.872 — 92
7) 68.251 — 68
8) 66.784 — 67
9) 90.883 — 91
10) 46.941 — 47
11) 58.711 — 59
12) 43.844 — 44

Round to the nearest tenths.

13) 67.068 — 67.1
14) 11.357 — 11.4
15) 41.793 — 41.8
16) 86.271 — 86.3
17) 67.803 — 67.8
18) 80.576 — 80.6
19) 44.998 — 45.0
20) 43.642 — 43.6
21) 92.212 — 92.2
22) 38.481 — 38.5
23) 71.344 — 71.3
24) 87.781 — 87.8

Round to the nearest hundreths.

25) 50.429 — 50.43
26) 18.387 — 18.39
27) 47.001 — 47.00
28) 96.195 — 96.20
29) 28.434 — 28.43
30) 34.027 — 34.03
31) 34.877 — 34.88
32) 57.622 — 57.62
33) 42.596 — 42.60
34) 64.892 — 64.89
35) 40.299 — 40.30
36) 37.814 — 37.81

Round to the nearest whole number.

1) 56.132 — 56
2) 15.828 — 16
3) 20.443 — 20
4) 83.984 — 84
5) 93.271 — 93
6) 78.407 — 78
7) 23.315 — 23
8) 64.102 — 64
9) 81.204 — 81
10) 21.478 — 21
11) 92.647 — 93
12) 50.936 — 51

Round to the nearest tenths.

13) 97.365 — 97.4
14) 95.054 — 95.1
15) 77.034 — 77.0
16) 84.018 — 84.0
17) 69.136 — 69.1
18) 26.452 — 26.5
19) 37.339 — 37.3
20) 47.617 — 47.6
21) 42.516 — 42.5
22) 47.977 — 48.0
23) 27.018 — 27.0
24) 22.597 — 22.6

Round to the nearest hundreths.

25) 48.903 — 48.90
26) 94.231 — 94.23
27) 89.458 — 89.46
28) 40.829 — 40.83
29) 22.645 — 22.65
30) 92.747 — 92.75
31) 30.428 — 30.43
32) 34.344 — 34.34
33) 64.808 — 64.81
34) 57.118 — 57.12
35) 12.423 — 12.42
36) 48.962 — 48.96

www.claymaze.com

Round to the nearest whole number.

1) 40.478 40
2) 31.385 31
3) 43.288 43
4) 33.002 33
5) 61.557 62
6) 45.428 45
7) 66.179 66
8) 44.742 45
9) 15.222 15
10) 30.737 31
11) 47.781 48
12) 38.653 39

Round to the nearest tenths.

13) 54.386 54.4
14) 35.893 35.9
15) 78.923 78.9
16) 25.639 25.6
17) 27.185 27.2
18) 90.692 90.7
19) 23.695 23.7
20) 61.997 62.0
21) 75.385 75.4
22) 23.442 23.4
23) 82.156 82.2
24) 94.202 94.2

Round to the nearest hundreths.

25) 67.175 67.18
26) 26.722 26.72
27) 83.421 83.42
28) 25.872 25.87
29) 80.054 80.05
30) 30.211 30.21
31) 65.616 65.62
32) 71.269 71.27
33) 65.944 65.94
34) 79.005 79.01
35) 83.538 83.54
36) 81.295 81.30

Round to the nearest whole number.

1) 62.884 63
2) 50.892 51
3) 59.848 60
4) 54.566 55
5) 50.215 50
6) 65.357 65
7) 61.395 61
8) 40.402 40
9) 35.437 35
10) 10.663 11
11) 53.542 54
12) 92.979 93

Round to the nearest tenths.

13) 51.758 51.8
14) 38.365 38.4
15) 65.378 65.4
16) 84.377 84.4
17) 55.734 55.7
18) 68.565 68.6
19) 28.036 28.0
20) 56.933 56.9
21) 65.375 65.4
22) 25.279 25.3
23) 76.535 76.5
24) 30.983 31.0

Round to the nearest hundreths.

25) 75.704 75.70
26) 81.714 81.71
27) 88.938 88.94
28) 11.448 11.45
29) 57.354 57.35
30) 16.644 16.64
31) 60.283 60.28
32) 18.616 18.62
33) 61.802 61.80
34) 21.787 21.79
35) 25.614 25.61
36) 82.793 82.79

Round to the nearest whole number.

1) 72.702 73
2) 80.635 81
3) 26.219 26
4) 99.148 99
5) 27.026 27
6) 88.196 88
7) 89.701 90
8) 97.679 98
9) 33.772 34
10) 14.314 14
11) 47.919 48
12) 82.297 82

Round to the nearest tenths.

13) 82.812 82.8
14) 14.002 14.0
15) 54.598 54.6
16) 51.948 51.9
17) 63.251 63.3
18) 65.032 65.0
19) 23.029 23.0
20) 85.052 85.1
21) 73.701 73.7
22) 95.516 95.5
23) 21.829 21.8
24) 90.394 90.4

Round to the nearest hundreths.

25) 39.122 39.12
26) 44.317 44.32
27) 27.935 27.94
28) 47.432 47.43
29) 82.051 82.05
30) 57.245 57.25
31) 61.534 61.53
32) 78.465 78.47
33) 32.051 32.05
34) 85.404 85.40
35) 45.927 45.93
36) 61.646 61.65

Round to the nearest whole number.

1) 62.776 63
2) 62.363 62
3) 55.647 56
4) 42.263 42
5) 74.483 74
6) 43.341 43
7) 81.252 81
8) 41.254 41
9) 43.918 44
10) 99.325 99
11) 40.019 40
12) 87.816 88

Round to the nearest tenths.

13) 44.105 44.1
14) 87.979 88.0
15) 65.253 65.3
16) 76.281 76.3
17) 14.017 14.0
18) 48.433 48.4
19) 42.299 42.3
20) 58.402 58.4
21) 79.592 79.6
22) 20.081 20.1
23) 44.132 44.1
24) 80.639 80.6

Round to the nearest hundreths.

25) 68.959 68.96
26) 28.719 28.72
27) 65.491 65.49
28) 81.147 81.15
29) 90.338 90.34
30) 23.039 23.04
31) 60.343 60.34
32) 45.374 45.37
33) 12.488 12.49
34) 97.537 97.54
35) 77.894 77.89
36) 55.262 55.26

Round to the nearest whole number.

1) 28.186 28
2) 34.121 34
3) 29.555 30
4) 57.693 58
5) 60.522 61
6) 21.879 22
7) 30.688 31
8) 39.644 40
9) 43.777 44
10) 84.016 84
11) 91.631 92
12) 27.684 28

Round to the nearest tenths.

13) 97.286 97.3
14) 56.336 56.3
15) 33.641 33.6
16) 62.862 62.9
17) 31.098 31.1
18) 68.635 68.6
19) 35.939 35.9
20) 28.847 28.8
21) 78.474 78.5
22) 16.002 16.0
23) 38.685 38.7
24) 12.502 12.5

Round to the nearest hundreths.

25) 10.929 10.93
26) 36.057 36.06
27) 41.643 41.64
28) 69.098 69.10
29) 55.923 55.92
30) 49.616 49.62
31) 82.057 82.06
32) 16.346 16.35
33) 58.184 58.18
34) 77.598 77.60
35) 32.929 32.93
36) 30.502 30.50

Round to the nearest whole number.

1) 14.645 15
2) 99.218 99
3) 99.625 100
4) 60.864 61
5) 92.275 92
6) 98.301 98
7) 27.828 28
8) 51.845 52
9) 15.227 15
10) 44.571 45
11) 81.959 82
12) 54.752 55

Round to the nearest tenths.

13) 58.907 58.9
14) 61.268 61.3
15) 51.853 51.9
16) 81.079 81.1
17) 21.034 21.0
18) 68.338 68.3
19) 12.579 12.6
20) 85.898 85.9
21) 62.252 62.3
22) 20.641 20.6
23) 53.552 53.6
24) 52.118 52.1

Round to the nearest hundreths.

25) 34.423 34.42
26) 47.206 47.21
27) 28.432 28.43
28) 87.172 87.17
29) 83.668 83.67
30) 16.129 16.13
31) 18.188 18.19
32) 39.977 39.98
33) 71.064 71.06
34) 17.174 17.17
35) 46.183 46.18
36) 45.196 45.20

www.claymaze.com

Round to the nearest whole number.

1) 15.196 __15__ 2) 53.683 __54__ 3) 35.428 __35__

4) 60.122 __60__ 5) 95.519 __96__ 6) 64.136 __64__

7) 53.438 __53__ 8) 62.452 __62__ 9) 69.217 __69__

10) 91.371 __91__ 11) 33.925 __34__ 12) 98.149 __98__

Round to the nearest tenths.

13) 83.353 __83.4__ 14) 97.948 __97.9__ 15) 16.595 __16.6__

16) 94.683 __94.7__ 17) 11.145 __11.1__ 18) 26.101 __26.1__

19) 10.211 __10.2__ 20) 41.376 __41.4__ 21) 37.861 __37.9__

22) 82.017 __82.0__ 23) 38.964 __39.0__ 24) 56.551 __56.6__

Round to the nearest hundreths.

25) 41.401 __41.40__ 26) 57.421 __52.42__ 27) 45.832 __45.83__

28) 64.293 __64.29__ 29) 53.322 __53.32__ 30) 83.534 __83.53__

31) 80.723 __80.72__ 32) 91.982 __91.98__ 33) 78.599 __78.60__

34) 26.791 __26.79__ 35) 97.257 __97.26__ 36) 87.245 __87.25__

Round to the nearest whole number.

1) 46.628 __47__ 2) 20.435 __20__ 3) 23.737 __24__

4) 86.238 __86__ 5) 81.123 __81__ 6) 48.736 __49__

7) 75.085 __75__ 8) 33.954 __34__ 9) 24.842 __25__

10) 54.171 __54__ 11) 22.807 __23__ 12) 24.012 __24__

Round to the nearest tenths.

13) 35.578 __35.6__ 14) 91.847 __91.8__ 15) 60.749 __60.7__

16) 33.837 __33.8__ 17) 89.916 __89.9__ 18) 67.798 __67.8__

19) 38.622 __38.6__ 20) 28.089 __28.1__ 21) 57.596 __57.6__

22) 82.435 __82.4__ 23) 34.804 __34.8__ 24) 73.235 __73.2__

Round to the nearest hundreths.

25) 82.602 __82.60__ 26) 49.308 __49.31__ 27) 79.374 __79.37__

28) 88.307 __88.31__ 29) 57.694 __57.69__ 30) 78.384 __78.38__

31) 10.372 __10.37__ 32) 61.091 __61.09__ 33) 67.121 __67.12__

34) 40.751 __40.75__ 35) 56.959 __56.96__ 36) 26.919 __26.92__

Write the decimals as percentages.

1) .68 __68%__ 2) .78 __78%__ 3) .85 __85%__ 4) .4 __40%__

5) .61 __61%__ 6) .97 __97%__ 7) .41 __41%__ 8) .07 __7%__

Write the percentages as decimals.

9) 38% __.38__ 10) 55% __.55__ 11) 70% __.7__ 12) 17% __.17__

13) 8% __.08__ 14) 15% __.15__ 15) 33% __.33__ 16) 36% __.36__

Calculate the percentages.

17) 47% of 54   18) 32% of 91   19) 92% of 94

25.38   29.12   86.48

20) 86% of 86   21) 68% of 35   22) 89% of 58

73.96   23.8   51.62

Write the decimals as percentages.

1) .9 __90%__ 2) .19 __19%__ 3) .36 __36%__ 4) .71 __71%__

5) .94 __94%__ 6) .38 __38%__ 7) .41 __41%__ 8) .97 __97%__

Write the percentages as decimals.

9) 40% __.4__ 10) 92% __.92__ 11) 65% __.65__ 12) 14% __.14__

13) 12% __.12__ 14) 85% __.85__ 15) 27% __.27__ 16) 5% __.05__

Calculate the percentages.

17) 97% of 19   18) 50% of 15   19) 39% of 39

18.43   7.5   15.21

20) 48% of 77   21) 82% of 49   22) 27% of 53

36.96   40.18   14.31

Write the decimals as percentages.

1) .38 __38%__ 2) .73 __73%__ 3) .23 __23%__ 4) .37 __37%__

5) .49 __49%__ 6) .86 __86%__ 7) .02 __2%__ 8) .31 __31%__

Write the percentages as decimals.

9) 54% __.54__ 10) 2% __.02__ 11) 43% __.43__ 12) 14% __.14__

13) 40% __.4__ 14) 44% __.44__ 15) 88% __.88__ 16) 52% __.52__

Calculate the percentages.

17) 62% of 62   18) 33% of 64   19) 55% of 72

38.44   21.12   39.6

20) 87% of 43   21) 65% of 85   22) 54% of 89

37.41   55.25   48.06

Write the decimals as percentages.

1) .35 __35%__ 2) .41 __41%__ 3) .44 __44%__ 4) .67 __67%__

5) .58 __58%__ 6) .43 __43%__ 7) .66 __66%__ 8) .15 __15%__

Write the percentages as decimals.

9) 69% __.69__ 10) 28% __.28__ 11) 51% __.51__ 12) 52% __.52__

13) 95% __.95__ 14) 96% __.96__ 15) 49% __.49__ 16) 32% __.32__

Calculate the percentages.

17) 17% of 63   18) 49% of 96   19) 2% of 38

10.71   47.04   .76

20) 93% of 34   21) 95% of 49   22) 85% of 60

31.62   46.55   51

Write the decimals as percentages.

1) .95 95%   2) .51 51%   3) .46 46%   4) .42 42%

5) .29 29%   6) .55 55%   7) .03 3%   8) .53 53%

Write the percentages as decimals.

9) 36% .36   10) 18% .18   11) 87% .87   12) 43% .43

13) 51% .51   14) 36% .36   15) 14% .14   16) 75% .75

Calculate the percentages.

17) 37% of 86   18) 66% of 87   19) 30% of 90

31.82   57.42   27

20) 98% of 82   21) 95% of 45   22) 9% of 35

80.36   42.75   3.15

Write the decimals as percentages.

1) .79 79%   2) .27 27%   3) .23 23%   4) .39 39%

5) .85 85%   6) .49 49%   7) .56 56%   8) .64 64%

Write the percentages as decimals.

9) 46% .46   10) 48% .48   11) 74% .74   12) 28% .28

13) 52% .52   14) 96% .96   15) 10% .1   16) 45% .45

Calculate the percentages.

17) 54% of 97   18) 26% of 69   19) 27% of 80

52.38   17.94   21.6

20) 28% of 15   21) 33% of 32   22) 76% of 10

4.2   10.56   7.6

Write the decimals as percentages.

1) .97 97%   2) .91 91%   3) .74 74%   4) .96 96%

5) .04 4%   6) .27 27%   7) .25 25%   8) .17 17%

Write the percentages as decimals.

9) 77% .77   10) 82% .82   11) 9% .09   12) 93% .93

13) 71% .71   14) 42% .42   15) 64% .64   16) 46% .46

Calculate the percentages.

17) 5% of 83   18) 50% of 57   19) 21% of 20

4.15   28.5   4.2

20) 11% of 80   21) 1% of 11   22) 24% of 75

8.8   .11   18

Write the decimals as percentages.

1) .85 85%   2) .63 63%   3) .13 13%   4) .93 93%

5) .49 49%   6) .45 45%   7) .61 61%   8) .22 22%

Write the percentages as decimals.

9) 60% .6   10) 95% .95   11) 79% .79   12) 88% .88

13) 4% .04   14) 1% .01   15) 46% .46   16) 20% .2

Calculate the percentages.

17) 84% of 95   18) 11% of 28   19) 46% of 76

79.8   3.08   34.96

20) 55% of 59   21) 3% of 49   22) 13% of 59

32.45   1.47   7.67

Write the decimals as percentages.

1) .6 60%   2) .54 54%   3) .3 30%   4) .32 32%

5) .82 82%   6) .41 41%   7) .86 86%   8) .15 15%

Write the percentages as decimals.

9) 41% .41   10) 72% .72   11) 79% .79   12) 88% .88

13) 25% .25   14) 12% .12   15) 61% .61   16) 19% .19

Calculate the percentages.

17) 85% of 23   18) 63% of 65   19) 71% of 64

19.55   40.95   45.44

20) 43% of 99   21) 49% of 40   22) 18% of 70

42.57   19.6   12.6

Write the decimals as percentages.

1) .94 94%   2) .41 41%   3) .76 76%   4) .07 7%

5) .38 38%   6) .93 93%   7) .78 78%   8) .8 80%

Write the percentages as decimals.

9) 32% .32   10) 37% .37   11) 82% .82   12) 46% .46

13) 96% .96   14) 57% .57   15) 65% .65   16) 35% .35

Calculate the percentages.

17) 75% of 76   18) 3% of 17   19) 84% of 15

57   .51   12.6

20) 11% of 17   21) 21% of 87   22) 8% of 34

1.87   18.27   2.72

www.claymaze.com

Write the decimals as percentages.

1) .69 __69%__ 2) .37 __37%__ 3) .73 __73%__ 4) .28 __28%__

5) .7 __70%__ 6) .11 __11%__ 7) .46 __46%__ 8) .03 __3%__

Write the percentages as decimals.

9) 88% __.88__ 10) 31% __.31__ 11) 35% __.35__ 12) 16% __.16__

13) 39% __.39__ 14) 50% __.5__ 15) 42% __.42__ 16) 98% __.98__

Calculate the percentages.

17) 50% of 68   18) 8% of 55   19) 68% of 45

34   4.4   30.6

20) 27% of 11   21) 43% of 10   22) 52% of 21

2.97   4.3   10.92

Made in the USA
Las Vegas, NV
13 March 2022